WHITAKER'S ALMANACK
QUIZ BOOK

GW00647747

A & C BLACK
LONDON

Whitaker's Almanack
Quiz Book

A & C BLACK
LONDON

A & C Black (Publishers) Ltd
37 Soho Square, London W1D
3QZ
Whitaker's Almanack published
annually since 1868
© A & C Black (Publishers) Ltd

ISBN 0-7136-7035-5

Designed by: Fiona Pike
Jacket photographs: © Corbis
Typeset in India by: Wordstop,
Madras, India
Printed and bound in the EU by:
William Clowes, Beccles, Suffolk,
Great Britain

EDITORIAL STAFF
Author: Nick Rennison
Editor-in-Chief: Lauren Simpson
Editor: Inna Ward

CONTENTS

INTRODUCTION

BY NICK RENNISON, AUTHOR

Never before has society been so obsessed with facts, statistics, general knowledge and trivia…and that's why we have published the first ever edition of the *Whitaker's Almanack Quiz Book*. With a growing abundance of television shows and magazines dedicated to quizzes, people can be found pitting their wits against each other on all manner of subjects just about everywhere - at home, at work or in the pub. There is no doubt that accumulating banks of useful (and useless!) information has become a national pastime…and it's compulsive!

If, like me, you are fanatical about facts and figures and have a thirst for general knowledge, you'll find it hard to put this book down. Whether you are a quiz compiler, a pub quiz addict or you simply love asking and answering questions, the *Whitaker's Almanack Quiz Book* provides the ultimate quiz challenge and is lots of fun for all the family. Covering a wide range of both general and esoteric topics you'll be able to test your knowledge on almost every conceivable subject.

HOW TO USE THIS BOOK

There are twelve categories, arranged alphabetically, and within each category there is a selection of quizzes, also arranged alphabetically. For example, under Language and Literature you'll find quizzes on Novels and Novelists, Poetry, Shakespeare and Weird Words. Turn to page 5 for a full list of contents.

Quizzes are categorised as Novice, Expert or Genius which correspond to easy (or not so easy!), medium and hard levels of difficulty. In addition, each category is accompanied by a number of brain images - one brain for Novice, two brains for Expert and three brains for the Genius category. These enable you to check the difficultly level of a particular quiz at a glance. I would like to add that I cannot be held responsible for any squabbles that may arise in regard to whether a quiz is easy, medium or difficult!

Each quiz comprises ten multiple-choice questions with three possible answers. The answers can be found at the end of each quiz so unlike other quiz books you don't need to turn the book upside down or trawl to the back for the solutions!

While I was compiling this book, many people suggested questions for inclusion. My thanks go especially to Andee Anantha, Giri Anantha (for his astonishing knowledge of sports, in particular football), Brenda Binns, Travis Elborough, Andy Miller, Eileen Rennison, Philip Rennison and John Thewlis. At A & C Black, Lauren Simpson and Inna Ward were very helpful, supportive and (above all) patient editors. Most of all I would like to thank Eve Gorton. She devised hundreds of questions for this book and, without her assistance and encouragement, I would not have been able to finish it.

Nick Rennison

The Whitaker's Almanack Quiz Book is compiled with the authority of its sister publication, Whitaker's Almanack, which has a 137-year tradition of providing authoritative reference material on almost every aspect of today's rapidly changing world.

BELIEFS

BELIEFS 1

EXPERT

1) Which religion was founded by Guru Nanak in the 15th century?
   a) Jainism
   b) Hinduism
   c) Sikhism

2) Before he founded the Church of Scientology, what career had L. Ron Hubbard pursued?
   a) Encyclopaedia salesman
   b) Science fiction writer
   c) Circus performer

3) Which religious group was founded by George Fox?
   a) The Methodists
   b) The Quakers
   c) The Seventh Day Adventists

4) How many theses did Martin Luther post on the door of the church at Wittenberg in 1517?
   a) 95
   b) 39
   c) 18

5) How are members of the Church of Jesus Christ of Latter Day Saints better known?
   a) Mormons
   b) Christian Scientists
   c) Jehovah's Witnesses

6) When does the Jewish Sabbath begin?
   a) Sunset on Friday
   b) Dawn on Saturday
   c) Midday on Saturday

7) What does the title Hajji signify when applied to a Muslim man?
   a) That he has made a pilgrimage to Mecca
   b) That he is the head of his family
   c) That he is an Imam

8) Which Jewish festival means, in translation, 'the head of the year'?
   a) Yom Kippur
   b) Rosh Hashanah
   c) Bar Mitzvah

9) Which gods form the Trimurti or triumvirate of principal gods of Hinduism?
   a) Krishna, Kali and Shiva
   b) Brahma, Vishnu and Shiva
   c) Krishna, Kali and Vishnu

10) Which of the following is *not* one of the Four Noble Truths of Buddhism?
   a) The cause of suffering is craving
   b) Existence is characterised by suffering
   c) Suffering enables one to acquire merit

Answers: 1c, 2b, 3b, 4a, 5a, 6a, 7a, 8b, 9b, 10c

BELIEFS 2

EXPERT

1) In which city did John Calvin establish a theocratic state in the 16th century?
   a) Geneva
   b) Zurich
   c) Toulouse

2) What was the name of the founder of the religious community at Taizé in France?
   a) Brother Robert
   b) Brother Roger
   c) Brother René

3) Which Christian author wrote a book called *The Imitation of Christ*?
   a) Thomas More
   b) Thomas Aquinas
   c) Thomas à Kempis

4) In the Orthodox church, what is an iconostasis?
   a) a wall that divides the nave from the sanctuary
   b) an image of the crucifixion
   c) a medieval movement aimed at destroying icons

5) Which saint's day falls on Boxing Day?
   a) St. Andrew
   b) St. Stephen
   c) St. Wenceslas

6) Which animal is usually associated with St. Mark?
   a) A winged leopard
   b) A winged horse
   c) A winged lion

7) How many Popes have there been named John? (Excluding the two John Pauls)
   a) Sixteen
   b) Twenty
   c) Twenty-three

8) Whom did Rowan Williams succeed as the Archbishop of Canterbury?
   a) George Carey
   b) Robert Runcie
   c) Donald Coggan

EXPERT

9) Which 20th century missionary is associated with the mission at Lambaréné in equatorial Africa?
   a) Mary Slessor
   b) Albert Schweitzer
   c) Mother Teresa

10) In which year did the Catholic church decree that the Pope is infallible when he speaks *ex cathedra*?
   a) 1054
   b) 1453
   c) 1870

Answers: 1a, 2b, 3c, 4a, 5b, 6c, 7c, 8a, 9b, 10c

BELIEFS 3

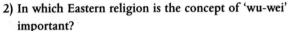

1) In which country is the pilgrimage site of Fatima where three children saw a vision of the Virgin Mary in 1917?
   a) Mexico
   b) Spain
   c) Portugal

2) In which Eastern religion is the concept of 'wu-wei' important?
   a) Shintoism
   b) Taoism
   c) Buddhism

GENIUS

3) In which country is the World Centre for the Baha'i faith?
   a) USA
   b) Lebanon
   c) Israel

4) What are modern followers of Zoroastrianism called?
   a) Parsees
   b) Jains
   c) Sikhs

5) Which biblical character is supposed to have founded Glastonbury Abbey?
   a) Joseph of Arimathea
   b) Lazarus
   c) St. Peter

6) In which religion is a text known in English as The Analects of central importance?
   a) Taoism
   b) Judaism
   c) Confucianism

7) In which religion is or was the Chi-Rho symbol used?
   a) Ancient Egyptian religion
   b) Christianity
   c) Judaism

8) Who described religion as 'the opium of the people'?
   a) Karl Marx
   b) Duke of Wellington
   c) George Bernard Shaw

9) What was founded in 1875 by Madame Blavatsky?
   a) Society of Friends
   b) London Spiritualist Church
   c) Theosophical Society

10) Which of the following is a name for the first five books of the Old Testament?
   a) Pentateuch
   b) Pentapolis
   c) Pentarchy

GENIUS

Answers: 1c, 2b, 3c, 4a, 5a, 6c, 7b, 8a, 9c, 10a

BELIEFS 4

GENIUS

1) In which Indian city is the Sikh Golden Temple?
   a) Agra
   b) Amritsar
   c) Delhi

2) Which religious movement was founded by Mary Baker Eddy in the 19th century?
   a) Christian Science
   b) Plymouth Brethren
   c) Primitive Baptists

3) What was the name of the angel that first visited Joseph Smith in 1823 to teach him about the Book of Mormon?
   a) Moroni
   b) Gabriel
   c) Michael

4) In religious terms what is 'satori'?
   a) A Sikh word for a temple
   b) A Hindu word for a religious commune
   c) A Buddhist word for enlightenment

5) In which religion do the 5 Ks have a central role to play?
   a) Shintoism
   b) Sikhism
   c) Taoism

6) Who were the Lohan?
   a) The eighteen original disciples of Buddha
   b) A group of contemplative monks in Tibet
   c) A group of angels in Mormon theology

7) In which religion are the gods known as kami?
   a) Taoism
   b) Confucianism
   c) Shintoism

GENIUS

8) In which century was Mohammed born?
   a) 8th century AD
   b) 7th century AD
   c) 6th century AD

9) In which religion do worshippers gather in a mandir?
   a) Sikhism
   b) Hinduism
   c) Shintoism

10) In which religion are there scriptures known as the
    Tipitaka?
    a) Buddhism
    b) Hinduism
    c) Taoism

Answers: 1b, 2a, 3a, 4c, 5b, 6a, 7c, 8c, 9b, 10a

CHRISTIANITY

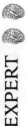

EXPERT

1) What significant event happened at Pentecost?
   a) The Last Supper
   b) The descent of the Holy Spirit
   c) The baptism of Jesus by St. John the Baptist

2) Why did Mary and Joseph go to Bethlehem for the birth of Jesus?
   a) To take part in a census
   b) To escape from King Herod
   c) To be with Mary's parents

3) Which day celebrates the entry of Jesus into Jerusalem?
   a) Advent Sunday
   b) Palm Sunday
   c) Jubilate Sunday

4) In the *Acts of the Apostles*, which city is credited with first giving the name 'Christians' to the followers of Jesus?
   a) Rome
   b) Constantinople
   c) Antioch

5) In the Catholic church, which of these sacraments can be administered to a believer only once?
   a) Marriage
   b) Confirmation
   c) Penance

6) Which did Jesus say was the first and greatest commandment?
   a) Love the Lord your God with all your heart and with all your soul and with all your mind
   b) You shall have no other gods before Me
   c) Love your neighbour as yourself

7) Which of these is nearest to the original meaning of the word 'apostle'?
   a) Disciple
   b) Messenger
   c) Reformer

EXPERT

8) Which two Anglican bishops were martyred near Balliol College, Oxford in 1555?
   a) Cranmer and Fisher
   b) Ridley and Latimer
   c) Cranmer and Ridley

9) To which of the following did St. Paul not write an epistle which is part of the New Testament?
   a) Thebans
   b) Galatians
   c) Thessalonians

10) Which of the following is not one of the original 'four doctors of the church'?
   a) St. Augustine
   b) St. Jerome
   c) St. Dominic

Answers: 1b, 2a, 3b, 4c, 5b, 6a, 7b, 8b, 9a, 10c

EASTERN RELIGIONS

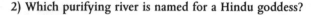

1) Which of the following sacred writings are the oldest among Hindu literature?
   a) Upanishads
   b) Bhagavad Gita
   c) Vedas

2) Which purifying river is named for a Hindu goddess?
   a) Ganges
   b) Brahmaputra
   c) Indus

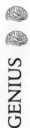

GENIUS

3) In which century did the Chinese philosopher and teacher Confucius live?
   a) 6th century BC
   b) 6th century AD
   c) 4th century BC

4) Where was Gautama Siddhartha Buddha born?
   a) Nepal
   b) Benares
   c) Sri Lanka

5) What decoration does the Hindu goddess Kali usually wear about her neck?
   a) A necklace of fire
   b) A garland of skulls
   c) A wreath of flowers

6) Which religion celebrates the Chichibu festival and the Gion festival?
   a) Taoism
   b) Jainism
   c) Shinto

7) What is the final factor of enlightenment in the teachings of Buddha?
   a) Awareness
   b) Tranquillity
   c) Equanimity

GENIUS

8) What is the Hindu belief that the actions in this life have a positive or negative result in the next called?
   a) Karma
   b) Nirvana
   c) Transmigration

9) Which Hindu god is said to be the preserver of the universe?
   a) Brahma
   b) Vishnu
   c) Indra

10) What is the Buddhist term for the state of inner rest and spiritual insight that a being reaches after finishing the complete cycle of reincarnations?
   a) Atman
   b) Nirvana
   c) Mahayana

Answers: 1c, 2a, 3a, 4a, 5b, 6c, 7c, 8a, 9b, 10b

GODS AND GODDESSES

In which religious system do the following gods and goddesses have a place?

GENIUS

1) **Hathor**
   a) Persian
   b) Egyptian
   c) Babylonian

2) **Viracocha**
   a) Hindu
   b) Aztec
   c) Inca

3) **Cernunnos**
   a) Etruscan
   b) Carthaginian
   c) Celtic

4) **Lofn**
   a) Viking
   b) Celtic
   c) Sumerian

5) **Lakshmi**
   a) Hindu
   b) Egyptian
   c) Shinto

6) **Mitra**
   a) Greek
   b) Babylonian
   c) Hindu

7) **Atar**
   a) Egyptian
   b) Persian
   c) Sumerian

8) **Gama**
   a) Shinto
   b) Hindu
   c) Persian

GENIUS

9) **Silenus**
   a) Greek
   b) Roman
   c) Etruscan

10) **Huitzilopochtli**
   a) Inca
   b) Mayan
   c) Aztec

Answers: 1b, 2c, 3c, 4a, 5a, 6c, 7b, 8a, 9a, 10c

ISLAM

1) What is a Sura?
 a) One of the sayings of the prophet
 b) A chapter of the Qur'an
 c) An Islamic mystic

2) How many times a day are Muslims required to pray?
 a) 3
 b) 4
 c) 5

3) What task does a muezzin perform?
 a) He maintains the fabric of the mosque
 b) He calls the believers to prayer
 c) He is a judge educated in the Sharia laws

4) What was the name of the daughter of the prophet Mohammed?
 a) Fatima
 b) Khadija
 c) Hafsa

5) Which angel passed the Qur'an down from heaven to Mohammed?
 a) Azrael
 b) Mikael
 c) Gabriel

EXPERT

6) What does Laylat al-Qadr (Night of Power or Night of Preciousness) commemorate?
   a) The birth of the prophet
   b) The giving of the Qur'an to the prophet
   c) The miraculous journey of the prophet from Mecca to Jerusalem

7) What is a Hafiz?
   a) One who has memorised the Qur'an
   b) One who teaches in a Muslim school
   c) One who has been on pilgrimage

EXPERT

8) A principal duty of Muslims is to make a pilgrimage to where?
   a) Medina
   b) Jerusalem
   c) Mecca

9) By what name are the five duties prescribed by the Qur'an also known?
   a) The five pillars
   b) The five principles
   c) The five foundations

10) What is the Shahada?
   a) Ritual washing
   b) The declaration of faith
   c) A prayer

Answers: 1b, 2c, 3b, 4a, 5c, 6b, 7a, 8c, 9a, 10b

'ISMS'

With which 'isms' would you most associate the following people?

1) **Friedrich Engels**
   a) Catholicism
   b) Marxism
   c) Monetarism

2) **Auguste Comte**
   a) Anarchism
   b) Positivism
   c) Existentialism

3) **Jean-Paul Sartre**
   a) Surrealism
   b) Logical Positivism
   c) Existentialism

4) **Sir Keith Joseph**
   a) Anarchism
   b) Socialism
   c) Thatcherism

5) **Lao-tse Tzu**
   a) Confucianism
   b) Buddhism
   c) Taoism

EXPERT

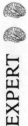

6) **Prince Peter Kropotkin**
   a) Anarchism
   b) Post-impressionism
   c) Catholicism

7) **Milton Friedman**
   a) Socialism
   b) Monetarism
   c) Keynesianism

8) **Andre Breton**
   a) Impressionism
   b) Cubism
   c) Surrealism

EXPERT

9) **A. J. Ayer**
   a) Logical Positivism
   b) Expressionism
   c) Monetarism

10) **Alfred Sisley**
   a) Impressionism
   b) Vorticism
   c) Dadaism

Answers: 1b, 2b, 3c, 4c, 5c, 6a, 7b, 8c, 9a, 10a

JUDAISM

1) **What is the name of the Jewish spring festival?**
   a) Rosh Hashannah
   b) Yom Kippur
   c) Pesach

2) **What does the word 'kosher' mean?**
   a) Traditional
   b) Fit or proper
   c) Bloodless

EXPERT

3) **Which of the following Jewish names derives from a word for 'priest'?**
   a) Bloom
   b) Levy
   c) Cohen

4) **What is a Shofar?**
   a) A type of Jewish candelabra
   b) A type of Jewish garment
   c) A type of Jewish musical instrument

5) **Which Jewish festival celebrates a boy's coming of age?**
   a) Yom Kippur
   b) Rosh Hashanah
   c) Bar Mitzvah

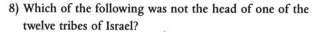

6) What is the Kabbalah?
   a) A set of Jewish prayer beads
   b) A word for the expected Jewish messiah
   c) A system of Jewish mystical beliefs

7) On one of the major Jewish fast days how long does fasting last?
   a) From sunset to sunrise
   b) From sunrise to sunset
   c) Twenty-five hours

8) Which of the following was not the head of one of the twelve tribes of Israel?
   a) Samuel
   b) Gad
   c) Naphtali

EXPERT

9) What does the Passover celebrate or commemorate?
   a) The exodus of the Jews from Egypt
   b) The start of a new year
   c) The building of the temple in Jerusalem

10) Which of the following is a name for the skullcap traditionally worn by Jewish males?
   a) Tzitzis
   b) Yarmulka
   c) Menorah

Answers: 1c, 2b, 3c, 4c, 5c, 6c, 7c, 8a, 9a, 10b

MYTHOLOGY 1

1) In Greek mythology who was the wife of Orpheus?
   a) Persephone
   b) Andromeda
   c) Eurydice

2) In Norse mythology who was the God of Mischief, son of Odin and the giantess Laufey?
   a) Baldur
   b) Loki
   c) Siegfried

NOVICE

3) In Greek mythology what was the name of the three-headed dog that guarded the entrance to the underworld?
   a) Cerberus
   b) Charon
   c) Polyphemus

4) Which Roman god is the equivalent to the Greek god Hephaestus?
   a) Dis
   b) Mars
   c) Vulcan

5) What is the name of the elephant-headed god in Hindu mythology?
   a) Hanuman
   b) Ganesha
   c) Shiva

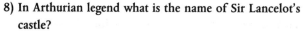

6) In Greek mythology what was the food of the gods?
   a) Ambrosia
   b) Nectar
   c) Manna

7) In Norse mythology where are the souls of heroes slain in battle taken?
   a) Ragnarok
   b) Valhalla
   c) Yggdrasil

NOVICE

8) In Arthurian legend what is the name of Sir Lancelot's castle?
   a) Siege Perilous
   b) Camelot
   c) Joyous Gard

9) Who was the feathered serpent deity of Aztec mythology?
   a) Popocatepetl
   b) Tenochtitlan
   c) Quetzalcoatl

10) In Greek mythology what was the name of the father of Achilles?
   a) Peleus
   b) Aegeus
   c) Heracles

Answers: 1c, 2b, 3a, 4c, 5b, 6a, 7b, 8c, 9c, 10a

MYTHOLOGY 2

EXPERT

1) In Greek mythology who was transformed into a spider after losing a weaving contest with the goddess Athena?
   a) Ariadne
   b) Arachne
   c) Atalanta

2) Which god of ancient Egypt was believed to be responsible for weighing the souls of the dead?
   a) Osiris
   b) Anubis
   c) Horus

3) Which god of Egyptian mythology murdered his brother and scattered his remains throughout Egypt?
   a) Set
   b) Horus
   c) Osiris

4) She is known as Helen of Troy but where did she come from originally?
   a) Athens
   b) Arcadia
   c) Sparta

5) In Greek legend Paris had to give an apple to the most beautiful of three goddesses. To which goddess did he give it?
   a) Athena
   b) Aphrodite
   c) Hera

6) In Greek mythology Zeus was the father of Heracles. Who was his mother?
   a) Leda
   b) Europa
   c) Alcmene

7) With what weapon is the Norse god Odin most often associated?
   a) Hammer
   b) Sword
   c) Spear

8) For whom was Ahura-Mazda the supreme god in the pantheon?
   a) The Egyptians
   b) The Assyrians
   c) The Persians

EXPERT

9) In Greek mythology what gift did Prometheus bring to mankind?
   a) Water
   b) Fire
   c) Eternal souls

10) In Arthurian legend what was the name of King Arthur's father?
    a) Uther Pendragon
    b) Pellinore
    c) Merlin

Answers: 1b, 2b, 3a, 4c, 5b, 6c, 7c, 8c, 9b, 10a

PHILOSOPHY 1

1) Which work by which philosopher advocates an ideal state based on rational order, ruled by philosopher kings?
   a) Nietzsche's *Thus Spake Zarathustra*
   b) Plato's *Republic*
   c) Machiavelli's *The Prince*

2) Which Greek philosopher was sentenced to death and committed suicide by taking poison?
   a) Aristotle
   b) Socrates
   c) Plato

3) What was the nationality of the philosopher S. A. Kierkegaard?
   a) Danish
   b) German
   c) Dutch

4) Which philosopher was the tutor of Alexander the Great?
   a) Plato
   b) Pythagoras
   c) Aristotle

5) Which French philosopher wrote *Being and Nothingness*?
   a) Jean-Paul Sartre
   b) Jacques Derrida
   c) René Descartes

NOVICE

6) Which British philosopher also held the titles of Baron Verulam and Viscount of St. Albans?
   a) John Stuart Mill
   b) Francis Bacon
   c) Bertrand Russell

7) Which of the following is the title of a book by Friedrich Nietzsche?
   a) *The Gay Science*
   b) *Moses and Monotheism*
   c) *Madness and Civilisation*

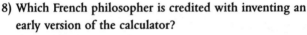

8) Which French philosopher is credited with inventing an early version of the calculator?
   a) René Descartes
   b) Denis Diderot
   c) Blaise Pascal

9) With which school of philosophy are Ludwig Wittgenstein and A. J. Ayer associated?
   a) Dialectical materialism
   b) Logical positivism
   c) Existentialism

10) Which philosopher wrote *Critique of Pure Reason*?
   a) Immanuel Kant
   b) Georg Friedrich Hegel
   c) Arthur Schopenhauer

Answers: 1b, 2b, 3a, 4c, 5a, 6b, 7a, 8c, 9b, 10a

NOVICE

PHILOSOPHY 2

GENIUS

1) Which American philosopher wrote *A Theory of Justice*, first published in 1971?
   a) Richard Rorty
   b) John Dewey
   c) John Rawls

2) Of what is epistemology the study?
   a) Logic
   b) The theory of knowledge
   c) Ethics

3) Who once wrote, 'Philosophy is at once the most sublime and the most trivial of human pursuits'?
   a) William James
   b) George Bernard Shaw
   c) Dr Johnson

4) In which city did René Descartes die?
   a) Paris
   b) Rome
   c) Stockholm

5) Which 20th century philosopher was shot dead by one of his students?
   a) Moritz Schlick
   b) Michel Foucault
   c) Karl Popper

6) Which 20th century philosopher murdered his wife?
   a) Jacques Derrida
   b) Jean-Paul Sartre
   c) Louis Althusser

7) What is the name of the school of philosophical thought
   derived from the ideas of Thomas Aquinas?
   a) Aquinarianism
   b) Thomistic philosophy
   c) Aquinistics

8) Which German philosopher wrote *Being and Time*?
   a) Martin Heidegger
   b) Immanuel Kant
   c) Edmund Husserl

GENIUS

9) Who wrote that, 'The philosophers have only interpreted
   the world in various ways; the point is to change it'?
   a) Lenin
   b) Mao-tse-Tung
   c) Karl Marx

10) Which English philosopher was born in Malmesbury in
    1588?
    a) John Locke
    b) Francis Bacon
    c) Thomas Hobbes

Answers: 1c, 2b, 3a, 4c, 5a, 6c, 7b, 8a, 9c, 10c

RELIGIOUS LEADERS

1) What was the name of the first Archbishop of Canterbury?
   a) Jerome
   b) Ambrose
   c) Augustine

2) Of which faith was a Persian prophet known as the Báb a forerunner?
   a) Buddhism
   b) Zoroastrianism
   c) Baha'i Faith

3) Who was Pope during the Second World War?
   a) Pius X
   b) Pius XI
   c) Pius XII

4) Which contemporary religious movement was founded by Li Hongzhi?
   a) Unification Church
   b) Falun Gong
   c) Aum Shinrikyo

5) What was the name of the leader of the Russian Orthodox Church in Britain who died in 2003?
   a) Metropolitan Anthony
   b) Metropolitan Anatoly
   c) Metropolitan Peter

EXPERT

6) By what name is the Protestant reformer Philip Schwarzerd usually known?
   a) Albertus Magnus
   b) Melanchthon
   c) Zwingli

7) Which Christian saint was the first to formulate a set of rules for monastic life?
   a) St. Benedict
   b) St. Francis of Assisi
   c) St. Bernard of Clairvaux

EXPERT

8) Of which religion is Mahavira considered to be the founder?
   a) Zoroastrianism
   b) Jainism
   c) Sikhism

9) How did the founder of the Mormon religion, Joseph Smith, meet his death?
   a) He was lynched by a mob
   b) He drowned in a freak flood
   c) He was killed in a fire at the first Mormon temple

10) What was the name of the first caliph, chosen to rule the Muslims after the death of Mohammed?
   a) Ali
   b) Haroun al-Rashid
   c) Abu-Bakr

Answers: 1c, 2c, 3c, 4b, 5a, 6b, 7a, 8b, 9a, 10c

BUSINESS
AND
POLITICS

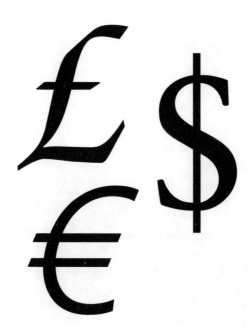

ADVERTISING SLOGANS

NOVICE

1) Which sportswear manufacturer uses the slogan "Just do it"?
   a) Reebok
   b) Nike
   c) Adidas

2) When was the famous slogan "Guinness is Good for You" first used?
   a) 1920s
   b) 1930s
   c) 1940s

3) Which company advised customers to "Put a Tiger in Your Tank" in the 1960s?
   a) Shell
   b) BP
   c) Esso

4) Which celebrity was used by John Smith's Bitter in their "No Nonsense" advertising campaign in the 1990s?
   a) Gary Lineker
   b) Alan Davies
   c) Jack Dee

5) Why did Heinz drop the "Beanz Meanz Heinz" slogan after using it for thirty years?
   a) They had received too many complaints about the misspellings
   b) They wanted to ensure its brand was associated with more than just baked beans
   c) The Trading Standards Authority felt that the slogan was misleading

6) The slogan "The future's bright, the future's orange" advertises what product?
   a) A soft drink
   b) Mobile communications
   c) On-line banking

7) Which slogan, still in use today, first advertised De Beers in the 1930s?
   a) When you care enough to give the very best
   b) A diamond is forever
   c) If you've got it, flaunt it

8) Which company asked "Where do you want to go today?"
   a) Thomas Cook
   b) Microsoft
   c) Volkswagen

9) Who was the famous face and voice in the "Cadbury's Fruit and Nut Case" TV advertisements in 1985?
   a) Frank Muir
   b) Dennis Norden
   c) Jeremy Beadle

10) Which drink was claimed to "refresh the parts other beers cannot reach"?
    a) Carling Black Label
    b) Carlsberg
    c) Heineken

NOVICE

Answers: 1b, 2a, 3c, 4c, 5b, 6b, 7b, 8b, 9a, 10c

BRITISH PARLIAMENT

1) **What is the effect of the Speaker 'naming' a member of Parliament?**
   a) The member may then address the House
   b) The member must leave the House immediately and resign his seat
   c) The member may be suspended for a period, during which he leaves the House

2) **Who was the Leader of the Conservative party at the beginning of the Second World War?**
   a) Stanley Baldwin
   b) Neville Chamberlain
   c) David Lloyd George

3) **What is the formal title of the Government Chief Whip?**
   a) Parliamentary Secretary to the Treasury
   b) The Father of the House
   c) The Under-secretary to the Cabinet

4) **Who was the first female Speaker of the House of Commons?**
   a) Bessie Braddock
   b) Nancy Astor
   c) Betty Boothroyd

5) **Who was the leader of the British Liberal party at the start of the Falklands War?**
   a) Jeremy Thorpe
   b) David Steel
   c) Paddy Ashdown

6) **Who was Home Secretary in 1910?**
   a) Winston Churchill
   b) Herbert Gladstone
   c) Reginald McKenna

7) **Who was the first Labour Prime Minister?**
   a) Clement Atlee
   b) Harold Wilson
   c) Ramsay MacDonald

8) **How many British Prime Ministers were in office between 1900 and 2000?**
   a) 15
   b) 20
   c) 25

EXPERT

9) **What form does a 'three-line whip' take?**
   a) It is a memo three lines in length
   b) It is an item in the weekly circular underlined three times
   c) It is a notice requiring members to vote at least three times

10) **Who presides over the election of a new Speaker of the House of Commons?**
    a) The previous Speaker
    b) The Father of the House
    c) The Prime Minister

Answers: 1c, 2b, 3a, 4c, 5b, 6a, 7c, 8b, 9b, 10b

BRITISH POLITICS

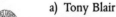

NOVICE

1) Which of the following was not a founding member of the SDP?
   a) Shirley Williams
   b) Roy Jenkins
   c) David Steel

2) In 1992 who succeeded Neil Kinnock as leader of the Labour Party?
   a) Tony Blair
   b) Michael Foot
   c) John Smith

3) In which year was Margaret Thatcher first elected Prime Minister?
   a) 1978
   b) 1979
   c) 1980

4) Which well-known politician is MP for the constituency of Dunfermline East?
   a) Gordon Brown
   b) Peter Mandelson
   c) Michael Howard

5) Who took the Enfield Southgate constituency from Michael Portillo in the 1997 general election?
   a) Stephen Twigg
   b) Diane Abbott
   c) Chris Bryant

6) Which parliamentary constituency did Alan Clark
represent at the time of his death in 1999?
a) Plymouth Sutton
b) Kensington and Chelsea
c) Billericay

7) Who famously said of Michael Howard that, 'There's
something of the night about him'?
a) Clare Short
b) Dennis Skinner
c) Ann Widdecombe

NOVICE

8) For which union did John Prescott work as a full-time
official before entering parliament?
a) National Union of Miners
b) National Union of Seamen
c) National Union of Teachers

9) Who was the last British Foreign Secretary to die while in
office?
a) George Brown
b) Anthony Eden
c) Anthony Crosland

10) What is the nickname of Dennis Skinner MP?
a) The Beast of Bolsover
b) The Derbyshire Demon
c) Dennis the Menace

Answers: 1c, 2c, 3b, 4a, 5a, 6b, 7c, 8b, 9c, 10a

BRITISH PRIME MINISTERS 1

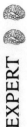

EXPERT

1) What is Margaret Thatcher's middle name?
   a) Helen
   b) Harriet
   c) Hilda

2) Which of the following was Prime Minister during the American War of Independence?
   a) Lord North
   b) Lord Melbourne
   c) Earl Grey

3) Who was Prime Minister at the start of World War One?
   a) David Lloyd George
   b) Herbert Henry Asquith
   c) Arthur Balfour

4) Of the eleven Prime Ministers since 1945 how many have been graduates of Oxford University?
   a) 3
   b) 6
   c) 8

5) Which Prime Minister was originally called Archibald Philip Primrose?
   a) Lord Rosebery
   b) Lord Salisbury
   c) Lord Palmerston

EXPERT

6) Which of the following was Prime Minister at the time of the Suez Crisis?
   a) Clement Attlee
   b) Anthony Eden
   c) Sir Alec Douglas-Home

7) Which Prime Minister became the Earl of Avon?
   a) Andrew Bonar Law
   b) Stanley Baldwin
   c) Anthony Eden

8) Which Prime Minister served the shortest time in office, dying less than four months after being appointed?
   a) Sir Robert Peel
   b) George Canning
   c) Viscount Goderich

9) Who was Prime Minister when Queen Victoria died?
   a) William Gladstone
   b) Lord Salisbury
   c) Lord Rosebery

10) What was the name of the rock band in which Tony Blair played when he was at Oxford?
   a) Ugly Rumours
   b) Vile Bodies
   c) Dirty Secrets

Answers: 1c, 2a, 3b, 4c, 5a, 6b, 7c, 8b, 9b, 10a

BRITISH PRIME MINISTERS 2

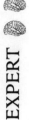

EXPERT

1) Who was the last Liberal Prime Minister of Great Britain?
   a) David Lloyd George
   b) Stanley Baldwin
   c) Henry Campbell-Bannerman

2) At what age did Pitt the Younger become Prime Minister?
   a) 24
   b) 26
   c) 28

3) What is Tony Blair's parliamentary constituency called?
   a) Kensington and Chelsea
   b) Islington South
   c) Sedgefield

4) Which of the following was serving as Prime Minister at the age of 84?
   a) William Gladstone
   b) Lord Salisbury
   c) Winston Churchill

5) Which of the following Prime Ministers was born outside Britain?
   a) Andrew Bonar Law
   b) Stanley Baldwin
   c) Anthony Eden

6) **Which Prime Minister became the Earl of Stockton?**
   a) Clement Attlee
   b) Harold Macmillan
   c) Ramsay MacDonald

7) **Who was the only British Prime Minister to be assassinated?**
   a) Sir Robert Peel
   b) Spencer Perceval
   c) Lord Liverpool

8) **What relation was Arthur Balfour to an earlier Prime Minister, Lord Salisbury?**
   a) Grandson
   b) Cousin
   c) Nephew

EXPERT

9) **Which future Prime Minister was forced to leave a heated public meeting about the Boer War disguised as a policeman?**
   a) Arthur Balfour
   b) David Lloyd George
   c) Winston Churchill

10) **Who was Prime Minister when Britain joined the European Common Market in 1973?**
   a) Harold Wilson
   b) Edward Heath
   c) James Callaghan

Answers: 1a, 2a, 3c, 4a, 5a, 6b, 7b, 8c, 9b, 10b

BUSINESS ACRONYMS

In the world of business and finance what do the following acronyms mean?

1) **WTO**
   a) World Trade Organisation
   b) Workers' Trade Organisation
   c) World Transport Organisation

NOVICE

2) **ERM**
   a) External Retail Market
   b) Exchange Rate Mechanism
   c) European Regional Market

3) **CBI**
   a) Congress of British Industry
   b) Confederation of British Industry
   c) Consolidated British Industries

4) **CAP**
   a) Common Agricultural Policy
   b) Community Agricultural Programme
   c) Confederation of Agricultural Producers

5) **EFTA**
   a) English Free Trade Association
   b) European Fair Trading Association
   c) European Free Trade Association

6) NASDAQ
a) National Association of Securities Dealers Automated Quotation
b) North American Securities Dealers Automated Quotation
c) North Atlantic Securities Dealers Automated Quotation

7) HSBC
a) Hong Kong and Shanghai Banking Corporation
b) Hang Seng Banking Corporation
c) High Street Banking Corporation

8) CEO
a) Corporate Executive Officer
b) Company Executive Officer
c) Chief Executive Officer

9) IBM
a) International Business Machines
b) Incorporated Business Machines
c) Integrated Business Machines

10) GmbH
a) Gemeindung mit bestellter Hafter
b) Gesellschaft mit beschränkter Haftung
c) Gesellschaft mit bestellter Haftung

NOVICE

BUSINESS

1) Which bank is in charge of the European Single Monetary Policy?
   a) The European Central Bank
   b) The European Investment Bank
   c) The Bundesbank

2) Where was the world's first stock exchange established?
   a) London
   b) Antwerp
   c) Florence

NOVICE

3) In which city is the headquarters of the International Monetary Fund?
   a) Paris
   b) Washington D. C.
   c) Zurich

4) On which stock market is the share index known as the Hang Seng?
   a) Shanghai
   b) Tokyo
   c) Hong Kong

5) What is the name of the 'rogue trader' whose activities led to the collapse of Barings Bank in 1995?
   a) Nick Leeson
   b) Nick Hancock
   c) Nick Rennison

6) In what year was the Dow-Jones Average first used on the New York Stock Exchange?
   a) 1896
   b) 1929
   c) 1975

7) Which American politician was once CEO of Halliburton, a company much involved in the rebuilding of Iraq after the second Gulf War?
   a) Colin Powell
   b) Donald Rumsfeld
   c) Dick Cheney

NOVICE

8) Which American company collapsed in December 2001 in what was the largest bankruptcy in US history?
   a) Exxon
   b) Enron
   c) General Motors

9) What did the Nintendo company make when it first started business in the 19th century?
   a) Confectionery
   b) Playing cards
   c) Dolls

10) On which London street does the Bank of England stand?
   a) Chancery Lane
   b) Cheapside
   c) Threadneedle Street

Answers: 1a, 2b, 3b, 4c, 5a, 6a, 7c, 8b, 9b, 10c

CURRENCIES

In which countries would you spend the following currencies?

1) The Lek
   a) Bulgaria
   b) Albania
   c) Slovakia

2) The Tugrik
   a) Mongolia
   b) Afghanistan
   c) Libya

EXPERT

3) The Forint
   a) Hungary
   b) Czech Republic
   c) Netherlands

4) The Quetzal
   a) El Salvador
   b) Ecuador
   c) Guatemala

5) The Ringgit
   a) Indonesia
   b) Malaysia
   c) Singapore

6) **The Zloty**
   a) Poland
   b) Ukraine
   c) Georgia

7) **The Guarani**
   a) Paraguay
   b) Colombia
   c) Mozambique

8) **The Colon**
   a) Mexico
   b) Honduras
   c) Costa Rica

9) **The Pula**
   a) Rwanda
   b) Botswana
   c) Central African Republic

10) **The Ngultrum**
   a) Myanmar
   b) Nepal
   c) Bhutan

EXPERT

Answers: 1b, 2a, 3a, 4c, 5b, 6a, 7a, 8c, 9b, 10c

ECONOMICS AND ECONOMISTS

1) Which 18th century philosopher and economist wrote
The Wealth of Nations?
a) Thomas Malthus
b) Adam Smith
c) David Ricardo

2) In what year was the Nobel Prize for Economics first
awarded?
a) 1901
b) 1935
c) 1969

3) What did Thomas Carlyle call economics (or political
economy, as it was known in his day)?
a) The doubtful science
b) The dreadful science
c) The dismal science

4) Which of the following people attended the London
School of Economics?
a) Pete Townsend
b) Mick Jagger
c) Elton John

5) Who wrote *The Affluent Society*, first published in the
1950s?
a) J. K. Galbraith
b) Friedrich Hayek
c) Milton Friedman

6) In economics what does GDP stand for?
   a) Gross Deficit Payment
   b) Government Deficit Payment
   c) Gross Domestic Product

7) Which of the following words was coined in 1968 by Karl Brunner to describe the economic theories of Milton Friedman?
   a) Macroeconomics
   b) Monetarism
   c) Short-termism

8) What nationality is the Nobel Prize-winning economist Paul Samuelson?
   a) British
   b) German
   c) American

9) Of which literary and artistic group was the economist John Maynard Keynes a member?
   a) Bloomsbury Group
   b) Surrealists
   c) Futurists

10) Which Austrian economist and political thinker wrote *The Road to Serfdom*?
   a) Ludwig von Mises
   b) Ludwig Lachmann
   c) Friedrich Hayek

Answers: 1b, 2c, 3c, 4b, 5a, 6c, 7b, 8c, 9a, 10c

PEOPLE IN BUSINESS

NOVICE

1) Where was Jesse Boot, founder of Boots, the chemist, born?
   a) Nottingham
   b) Norwich
   c) Northampton

2) Which high street chain was bought by Philip Green in May 2000?
   a) Marks and Spencer
   b) British Home Stores
   c) Littlewoods

3) Who started his business career with a successful 'five and dime' store in Lancaster, Pennsylvania?
   a) Frank Woolworth
   b) Richard W. Sears
   c) Joseph Bloomingdale

4) In what year was Richard Branson born?
   a) 1945
   b) 1948
   c) 1950

5) Which software company was founded by a Harvard dropout in 1975?
   a) IBM
   b) Apple Computers
   c) Microsoft

6) Who founded The Body Shop?
   a) Anita Roddick
   b) Nicola Horlick
   c) Zandra Rhodes

7) Which football club did Mohammed Al Fayed buy in 1997?
   a) Chelsea
   b) Fulham
   c) Tottenham Hotspur

8) In which year was Sainsbury's founded by John James and Mary Ann Sainsbury?
   a) 1869
   b) 1900
   c) 1952

NOVICE

9) Which giant American company was run by a father and son, both called Thomas Watson, from the time of the First World War to the 1970s?
   a) AT & T
   b) General Motors
   c) IBM

10) Which supermarket chain was founded by Jack Cohen in 1929?
   a) Safeway
   b) Tesco
   c) Asda

Answers: 1a, 2b, 3a, 4c, 5c, 6a, 7b, 8a, 9c, 10b

POLITICAL QUOTATIONS

1) Which country did Churchill describe as 'a riddle wrapped in a mystery inside an enigma'?
   a) Russia
   b) Germany
   c) France

2) Which Prime Minister famously said that the nation had 'never had it so good'?
   a) Margaret Thatcher
   b) Harold Wilson
   c) Harold Macmillan

3) Who described politics as 'the art of the possible'?
   a) Benjamin Disraeli
   b) Otto von Bismarck
   c) Niccolo Machiavelli

4) Which US president said that there could be 'no whitewash at the White House'?
   a) Gerald Ford
   b) Bill Clinton
   c) Richard Nixon

5) Who, in parliament, owned up to 'the atrocious crime of being a young man'?
   a) William Pitt the Elder
   b) William Pitt the Younger
   c) Tony Blair

EXPERT

6) What event caused the British Foreign Secretary, Sir Edward Grey, to remark that 'the lamps are going out all over Europe'?
   a) The death of Gladstone
   b) The death of Queen Victoria
   c) The outbreak of the First World War

7) Which Labour politician, according to Simon Hoggart, 'can skulk in broad daylight'?
   a) Robin Cook
   b) Peter Mandelson
   c) Gordon Brown

EXPERT

8) According to the British politician Morgan Phillips, the Labour Party owes more to what than to Marxism?
   a) Trade Unionism
   b) Methodism
   c) Liberalism

9) Who said that a politician 'is a person who approaches every subject with an open mouth'?
   a) Adlai Stevenson
   b) Gore Vidal
   c) Peter Cook

10) Who wrote that 'the broad mass of a nation . . . . will more easily fall victim to a big lie than to a small one'?
   a) Josef Stalin
   b) Vladimir Lenin
   c) Adolf Hitler

Answers: 1a, 2c, 3b, 4c, 5a, 6c, 7b, 8b, 9a, 10c

SPIES AND INTELLIGENCE

EXPERT

1) What is the name of the Israeli secret intelligence service?
   a) Mossad
   b) Eilat
   c) Knesset

2) Which of the following official positions did Sir Anthony Blunt hold at the time he was revealed as a Soviet spy in 1979?
   a) Poet Laureate
   b) Master of Trinity College, Cambridge
   c) Keeper of the Queen's Pictures

3) Which of the following scientists was convicted by a British court in 1950 of passing secrets to the Russians?
   a) Enrico Fermi
   b) Robert Oppenheimer
   c) Klaus Fuchs

4) What was the name of the secret coding device used by the Germans in World War II, which was broken by the British codebreakers at Bletchley Park?
   a) Enigma
   b) Playfair
   c) Wortschatz

5) Who was the Dutch woman executed by the French for espionage during the First World War?
   a) Anne Frank
   b) Mata Hari
   c) Fanny Blankers-Koen

6) Which French novelist wrote a famous pamphlet defending Alfred Dreyfus, who had been falsely convicted of spying for the Germans?
a) Emile Zola
b) Marcel Proust
c) Gustave Flaubert

7) Which of the following Soviet leaders was also once head of the KGB?
a) Leonid Brezhnev
b) Nikita Krushchev
c) Yuri Andropov

EXPERT

8) Which British officer was hanged as a spy by the Americans during the American War of Independence?
a) General Benedict Arnold
b) Major John André
c) Captain John Byng

9) What was the name of the first James Bond film?
a) *Dr No*
b) *From Russia with Love*
c) *Goldfinger*

10) What are the initials of the French foreign intelligence service?
a) DFSE
b) DGSE
c) OSS

Answers: 1a, 2c, 3c, 4a, 5b, 6a, 7c, 8b, 9a, 10b

US PRESIDENTS 1

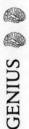
GENIUS

1) Who has served the shortest term in office as president?
   a) Martin van Buren
   b) William Henry Harrison
   c) Harry S. Truman

2) Which president later returned to public service as Chief Justice of the Supreme Court?
   a) Herbert Hoover
   b) Calvin Coolidge
   c) William Taft

3) Who was president during the Stock Market Crash of 1929?
   a) Herbert Hoover
   b) Warren G. Harding
   c) Calvin Coolidge

4) Who was the only president to earn a doctorate?
   a) John F. Kennedy
   b) Theodore Roosevelt
   c) Woodrow Wilson

5) Who was the first president whose son also became president?
   a) John Adams
   b) Andrew Johnson
   c) Theodore Roosevelt

£ $
€

GENIUS

6) Which president agreed to purchase Florida from Spain in 1919?
   a) James Monroe
   b) James Madison
   c) John Quincy Adams

7) Which president dedicated the Washington Monument in 1885?
   a) James A. Garfield
   b) Chester A. Arthur
   c) Rutherford B. Hayes

8) Who was the only president inaugurated in two cities: New York and Philadelphia?
   a) George Washington
   b) John Adams
   c) Thomas Jefferson

9) Which unmarried president had his niece, Harriet Lane, as his First Lady?
   a) Millard Fillmore
   b) James Buchanan
   c) William Henry Harrison

10) During whose term of office was the SALT agreement passed?
    a) Richard Nixon
    b) Jimmy Carter
    c) Gerald Ford

Answers: 1b, 2c, 3a, 4c, 5a, 6a, 7b, 8a, 9b, 10a

US PRESIDENTS 2

EXPERT

1) What is Bill Clinton's middle name?
   a) Franklin
   b) Lincoln
   c) Jefferson

2) Abraham Lincoln was the first American president to be
   assassinated. Who was the second?
   a) James Garfield
   b) William McKinley
   c) John F. Kennedy

3) The wife of which US president was called Lady Bird?
   a) Lyndon Johnson
   b) Richard Nixon
   c) Woodrow Wilson

4) Which US president wrote a book called *The Rough Riders?*
   a) Franklin Roosevelt
   b) Theodore Roosevelt
   c) Calvin Coolidge

5) What was the name given to the political scandal of the
   1920s that marred the presidency of Warren Harding?
   a) The Whiskey Ring
   b) The Maundy Gregory Affair
   c) The Teapot Dome Scandal

6) **Of what US state was Ronald Reagan governor?**
   a) Texas
   b) California
   c) Idaho

7) **Which of the following statements about Charles Dawes, Vice-President to Calvin Coolidge in the 1920s, is true?**
   a) He was a member of a religious sect
   b) He wrote the music for a Cliff Richard song
   c) He invented an early form of breathalyser

8) **What was the nickname of the 7th President Andrew Jackson?**
   a) Old Rough and Ready
   b) Old Man Eloquent
   c) Old Hickory

9) **Which US president sent Lewis and Clark on their famous expedition to explore the American continent?**
   a) Thomas Jefferson
   b) James Madison
   c) John Quincy Adams

10) **Who was the first US president to be impeached by the House of Representatives?**
   a) Bill Clinton
   b) Andrew Johnson
   c) Richard Nixon

EXPERT

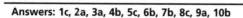

Answers: 1c, 2a, 3a, 4b, 5c, 6b, 7b, 8c, 9a, 10b

WORLD LEADERS

In which country have the following individuals been head of state or head of government in the last fifty years?

GENIUS

1) **Eduard Shevardnadze**
   a) Georgia
   b) Ukraine
   c) Uzbekistan

2) **Dom Mintoff**
   a) Malta
   b) Lebanon
   c) Greece

3) **Archbishop Makarios**
   a) Macedonia
   b) Greece
   c) Cyprus

4) **Anastasio Somoza**
   a) Guatemala
   b) Mexico
   c) Nicaragua

5) **Zulfikar Ali Bhutto**
   a) Nepal
   b) Pakistan
   c) Bangladesh

GENIUS

6) Alfredo Stroessner
   a) Colombia
   b) Paraguay
   c) Austria

7) Julius Nyerere
   a) Tanzania
   b) Uganda
   c) Kenya

8) Canaan Banana
   a) Mali
   b) Malawi
   c) Zimbabwe

9) Enver Hoxha
   a) Romania
   b) Albania
   c) Bulgaria

10) Gro Harlem Brundtland
   a) Norway
   b) Sweden
   c) Latvia

Answers: 1a, 2a, 3c, 4c, 5b, 6b, 7a, 8c, 9b, 10a

WORLD POLITICS 1

NOVICE

1) Of which country was Samora Machel president between 1975 and 1986?
   a) Mozambique
   b) Zaire
   c) Zambia

2) In which city did US warplanes accidentally bomb the Chinese embassy in May 1999?
   a) Kabul
   b) Khartoum
   c) Belgrade

3) Which of the following posts has been held by Jacques Santer and Jacques Delors?
   a) Prime Minister of Belgium
   b) President of the European Commission
   c) French ambassador to the United Nations

4) What were the names of the two ethnic groups involved in the Rwandan genocide of 1994?
   a) Hutu and Tutsi
   b) Masai and Kikuyu
   c) Ibo and Yoruba

5) Who became Ireland's first woman president in 1990?
   a) Mary Robertson
   b) Mary Robinson
   c) Mary McAleese

6) Which Israeli leader was assassinated in November 1995?
   a) Moshe Dayan
   b) Golda Meir
   c) Yitzhak Rabin

7) In which country does the International Criminal Tribunal for the Former Yugoslavia hold its sessions?
   a) The Netherlands
   b) Luxembourg
   c) Switzerland

NOVICE

8) In what year was Vladimir Putin first elected President of Russia?
   a) 1998
   b) 1999
   c) 2000

9) What was the name of Saddam Hussein's oldest son?
   a) Ali
   b) Qusay
   c) Uday

10) Who was the last British governor of Hong Kong?
   a) Chris Patten
   b) Robin Cook
   c) Nigel Lawson

Answers: 1a, 2c, 3b, 4a, 5b, 6c, 7a, 8c, 9c, 10a

WORLD POLITICS 2

EXPERT

1) Who became the first Chancellor of a newly unified
   Germany in 1991?
   a) Helmut Kohl
   b) Gerhard Schroder
   c) Helmut Schmidt

2) In which country is the reigning monarch called Bhumibol?
   a) Bhutan
   b) Nepal
   c) Thailand

3) Which of the following islands remains an overseas
   territory of France and sends representatives to the
   National Assembly in Paris?
   a) Martinique
   b) Madagascar
   c) Mauritius

4) What is the name of the Italian political party founded by
   Silvio Berlusconi?
   a) Alleanza Nazionale
   b) Forza Italia
   c) Italia Libre

5) Who did John F. Kennedy defeat in the 1960 US
   presidential election?
   a) Richard Nixon
   b) Lyndon Johnson
   c) Barry Goldwater

6) Who shared the Nobel Peace Prize with Yasser Arafat and Yitzhak Rabin in 1994?
   a) Abba Eban
   b) Ariel Sharon
   c) Shimon Peres

7) Which of the following countries joined the EU in 2004?
   a) Slovakia
   b) Turkey
   c) Bulgaria

8) Before becoming President of Haiti in 1991 what was Jean Bertrand Aristide's occupation?
   a) Lawyer
   b) Priest
   c) Doctor

9) Who succeeded Nelson Mandela as President of South Africa?
   a) Mangosuthu Buthelezi
   b) Desmond Tutu
   c) Thabo Mbeki

10) In which country did Aung San Suu Kyi lead a party that won national elections while she was under house arrest?
   a) Burma (Myanmar)
   b) South Korea
   c) Cambodia

Answers: 1a, 2c, 3a, 4b, 5a, 6c, 7a, 8b, 9c, 10a

FILM, TV AND RADIO

ANIMALS ON TV

1) In an episode of which TV series does a much-loved Siberian hamster turn out to be a common or garden rat?
   a) *Fawlty Towers*
   b) *'Allo 'Allo*
   c) *Only Fools and Horses*

2) What was the name of Dr Who's electronic dog?
   a) Ared
   b) The Tardis Hound
   c) K9

3) In the *Teletubbies,* what real animals appear in almost every episode?
   a) A cat and a dog
   b) A group of wild rabbits
   c) A small herd of sheep

4) What type of dog was Rin Tin Tin?
   a) Alsatian (German Shepherd)
   b) Collie
   c) St. Bernard

5) In which TV series does the banjo-playing toad, Gabriel the Croaker appear?
   a) *Fingermouse*
   b) *Bagpuss*
   c) *The Clangers*

NOVICE

6) What is the name of the talking cat in *Sabrina the Teenage Witch*?
   a) Zelda
   b) Lucrezia
   c) Salem

7) What type of animals were Pinky and Perky?
   a) Mice
   b) Dogs
   c) Pigs

8) In *Roobarb and Custard* what colour is Roobarb the dog?
   a) Green
   b) Yellow
   c) Pink

9) What was the name of the Lone Ranger's horse?
   a) Trigger
   b) Champion
   c) Silver

10) To which fictional family does a dog called Santa's Little Helper belong?
    a) The Flintstones
    b) The Simpsons
    c) The Munsters

NOVICE

Answers: 1a, 2c, 3b, 4a, 5b, 6c, 7c, 8a, 9c, 10b

79

CARTOONS

1) Which of the following was the first feature-length animated film made by Walt Disney?
   a) *Fantasia*
   b) *Snow White*
   c) *Dumbo*

2) In the 2001 animated film *Shrek* who provided the voice for the donkey?
   a) Eddie Murphy
   b) Jim Carrey
   c) Tom Hanks

3) Which cartoon character has a dog called Muttley?
   a) Dick Dastardly
   b) Yogi Bear
   c) Bart Simpson

4) In what town do the Flintstones live?
   a) Boulderville
   b) Bedrock
   c) Great Rock

5) In *The Simpsons*, what is the name of the owner of the nuclear power plant in which Homer works?
   a) Montgomery Burns
   b) Ned Flanders
   c) Seymour Skinner

NOVICE

6) Which of the following cartoon characters was first created by E. C. Segar in the 1920s and went on to become the star of animated films produced by Max Fleischer?
a) Huckleberry Hound
b) Felix the Cat
c) Popeye

7) Which cartoon characters made their first appearance in a 1940 short called *Puss Gets the Boot*?
a) Sylvester and Tweety Pie
b) Tom and Jerry
c) Goofy and Pluto

8) Which character had three nephews called Hewey, Dewey and Louie?
a) Mickey Mouse
b) Donald Duck
c) Bugs Bunny

9) What is the name of the ship sailed by Captain Pugwash?
a) The Jolly Roger
b) The Golden Cutlass
c) The Black Pig

10) With whom did the Teenage Mutant Ninja Turtles share their names?
a) Italian Renaissance artists
b) Planets
c) American states

NOVICE

Answers: 1b, 2a, 3a, 4b, 5a, 6c, 7b, 8b, 9c, 10a

CHILDREN'S TV

1) On which farm did Worzel Gummidge live?
   a) Beaverbrook Farm
   b) Donnybrook Farm
   c) Scatterbrook Farm

2) In which decade did *Watch with Mother* finish?
   a) 1970s
   b) 1980s
   c) 1990s

NOVICE

3) What colour were the Smurfs?
   a) Red
   b) Blue
   c) Green

4) Which craft was piloted by Steve Zodiac?
   a) Fireball XL5
   b) Thunderbird 1
   c) Stingray

5) In *Trumpton*, who were Hugh, Pugh, Barney McGrew, Cuthbert, Dibble and Grubb?
   a) The village police force
   b) The village band
   c) The village fire brigade

6) Whose sidekick was called Penfold?
   a) The Flowerpot Men
   b) Dangermouse
   c) Supergran

7) Which of the following series was narrated by Bernard Cribbins?
   a) *The Wombles*
   b) *Thomas the Tank Engine*
   c) *Tales of the Riverbank*

8) Which musical instrument did Sooty play?
   a) Drums
   b) Xylophone
   c) Trumpet

9) Whose arch enemy was Texas Pete?
   a) Bagpuss
   b) Deputy Dawg
   c) Superted

10) Who created *Grange Hill*?
   a) Tony Warren
   b) Carla Lane
   c) Phil Redmond

NOVICE

Answers: 1c, 2b, 3b, 4a, 5c, 6b, 7a, 8b, 9c, 10c

FILM 1

NOVICE

1) In which country is the 1984 film *The Killing Fields* set?
   a) Russia
   b) Cambodia
   c) Vietnam

2) Who plays Truman in the 1998 film *The Truman Show*?
   a) Jim Carrey
   b) Tom Hanks
   c) Michael Keaton

3) Who directed the 1980 film *The Elephant Man*?
   a) Mel Brooks
   b) David Lynch
   c) Tim Burton

4) Basil Rathbone is best known for playing which character on screen?
   a) Tarzan
   b) Sherlock Holmes
   c) The Saint

5) To which movie was the 1990 film *The Two Jakes* a sequel?
   a) *Casablanca*
   b) *Chinatown*
   c) *Paris, Texas*

6) What is the name of the monster in the *Nightmare on Elm Street* series of horror films?
   a) Freddy Krueger
   b) Michael Myers
   c) Norman Bates

7) In which European city is Nicolas Roeg's 1973 film *Don't Look Now* largely set?
   a) Paris
   b) Prague
   c) Venice

8) Who played Luke Skywalker in the original 1977 *Star Wars* film?
   a) Harrison Ford
   b) David Prowse
   c) Mark Hamill

9) In the 1939 film of *The Wizard of Oz* which of the following characters was played by Bert Lahr?
   a) The Tin Man
   b) The Cowardly Lion
   c) The Scarecrow

10) What is the first name of Bond villain Goldfinger?
   a) Erno
   b) Fritz
   c) Auric

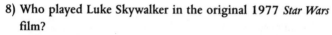

Answers: 1b, 2a, 3b, 4b, 5b, 6a, 7c, 8c, 9b, 10c

FILM 2

1) Who took the role of Catwoman in the 1992 film *Batman Returns*?
   a) Uma Thurman
   b) Michelle Pfeiffer
   c) Kim Basinger

2) Who directed the 2001 film *Moulin Rouge*?
   a) Baz Luhrmann
   b) Tim Burton
   c) Renny Harlin

3) What is Sigourney Weaver's real first name?
   a) Susan
   b) Simone
   c) Sharon

4) Who played the title role in the 1974 film version of *The Great Gatsby*?
   a) Paul Newman
   b) Ryan O'Neal
   c) Robert Redford

5) Which film actress married Humphrey Bogart in 1945?
   a) Lauren Bacall
   b) Kim Novak
   c) Katherine Hepburn

6) Which episode of the Star Wars series is *The Phantom Menace*?
   a) First
   b) Second
   c) Fourth

7) Who played Agent Smith in *The Matrix*?
   a) Laurence Fishburne
   b) Hugo Weaving
   c) Keanu Reeves

8) Who directed the 1946 film *It's a Wonderful Life*?
   a) Frank Capra
   b) Howard Hawks
   c) Preston Sturges

9) What is the profession of Hugh Grant's character in *Notting Hill*?
   a) Journalist
   b) Lawyer
   c) Bookseller

10) Which super-hero has been played on screen by Tobey Maguire?
   a) Superman
   b) Doc Savage
   c) Spiderman

NOVICE

Answers: 1b, 2a, 3a, 4c, 5a, 6a, 7b, 8a, 9c, 10c

FILM 3

1) Which 1976 film stars Sissy Spacek as a teenage girl with telekinetic powers?
   a) *Badlands*
   b) *Carrie*
   c) *Marnie*

2) Who created the special effects for the films *Jason and the Argonauts* and *The Golden Voyage of Sinbad*?
   a) Max Fleischer
   b) Willis O'Brien
   c) Ray Harryhausen

3) Who wrote the screenplay for the 1995 film version of Jane Austen's novel *Sense and Sensibility*?
   a) Emma Thompson
   b) Andrew Davies
   c) Malcolm Bradbury

4) Who played Sister Helen Prejean in the 1995 film *Dead Man Walking*?
   a) Susan Sarandon
   b) Geena Davis
   c) Glenn Close

5) Which US President was played by a British-born actor in a 1995 film?
   a) Franklin Roosevelt
   b) Abraham Lincoln
   c) Richard Nixon

NOVICE

6) Which veteran film-maker directed the John Cleese and Jamie Lee Curtis comedy *A Fish Called Wanda*?
   a) Jack Clayton
   b) Charles Crichton
   c) Michael Powell

7) Who played Douglas Fairbanks Sr in the 1992 film *Chaplin*?
   a) Kevin Costner
   b) Douglas Fairbanks Jr
   c) Kevin Kline

8) Which of the following was not one of the original founders of United Artists?
   a) D. W. Griffith
   b) Mack Sennett
   c) Charlie Chaplin

9) Where was Russell Crowe born?
   a) New Zealand
   b) New Guinea
   c) Australia

10) Who directed the 1936 Errol Flynn film *The Charge of the Light Brigade*?
   a) Michael Curtiz
   b) William Wyler
   c) George Cukor

NOVICE

Answers: 1b, 2c, 3a, 4a, 5c, 6b, 7c, 8b, 9a, 10a

FILM 4

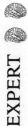

EXPERT

1) What nationality was the film director Krzystof Kieslowski?
   a) Russian
   b) Czech
   c) Polish

2) Which actor directed the film *A Bronx Tale*?
   a) Robert de Niro
   b) Dustin Hoffman
   c) Steve Buscemi

3) The 1995 film *Clueless*, starring Alicia Silverstone, is (loosely) based on which classic English novel?
   a) Jane Austen's *Emma*
   b) Charlotte Brontë's *Jane Eyre*
   c) Thomas Hardy's *Tess of the D'Urbervilles*

4) Which silent film star was known as 'America's Sweetheart'?
   a) Gloria Swanson
   b) Clara Bow
   c) Mary Pickford

5) For which film did John Wayne win his first and only Oscar for Best Actor?
   a) *Stagecoach*
   b) *The Searchers*
   c) *True Grit*

6) At which film festival do the makers of the Best Picture receive the Golden Bear award?
   a) Cannes
   b) Berlin
   c) Venice

7) Hitchcock's film *North by Northwest* reaches a dramatic climax at which American landmark?
   a) Mount Rushmore
   b) Empire State Building
   c) Niagara Falls

8) How old was James Dean when he died in a car crash in 1955?
   a) 24
   b) 28
   c) 32

9) Which of the film studios used to claim that they had 'more stars than there are in heaven'?
   a) Warner Brothers
   b) MGM
   c) Paramount

10) In what year was *Gone With the Wind* released?
   a) 1939
   b) 1938
   c) 1937

EXPERT

Answers: 1c, 2a, 3a, 4c, 5c, 6b, 7a, 8a, 9b, 10a

FILM 5

EXPERT

1) Who spoke the only line in Mel Brooks's 1976 film *Silent Movie*?
   a) Marty Feldman
   b) Mel Brooks
   c) Marcel Marceau

2) Who directed *Born on the Fourth of July* and *Talk Radio*?
   a) Ron Howard
   b) Oliver Stone
   c) Jonathan Demme

3) In which 1973 film did Steve McQueen play a prisoner trying to escape from a French penal colony?
   a) *Escape from Devil's Island*
   b) *The Great Escape*
   c) *Papillon*

4) Who played the Sheriff of Nottingham to Kevin Costner's Robin Hood in *Robin Hood, Prince of Thieves*?
   a) Alan Rickman
   b) Steven Berkoff
   c) Anthony Hopkins

5) Which film was made in 1922, starring Max Schreck, and in 1980, starring Klaus Kinski?
   a) *The Island of Dr Moreau*
   b) *Nosferatu*
   c) *Frankenstein*

6) What instrument does Robert de Niro play in the 1977 Martin Scorsese musical *New York, New York*?
   a) Piano
   b) Trumpet
   c) Saxophone

7) Which film, directed by David Lynch, stars Nicolas Cage and Laura Dern as a couple on the run?
   a) *Wild at Heart*
   b) *Lost Highway*
   c) *Blue Velvet*

EXPERT

8) Who played Wyatt Earp in the 1946 film *My Darling Clementine*?
   a) Henry Fonda
   b) James Stewart
   c) John Wayne

9) Who directed the 1973 film *Badlands*, starring Martin Sheen and Sissy Spacek?
   a) Brian de Palma
   b) Bob Rafelson
   c) Terrence Malick

10) Who provided the baby's voice in the 1989 film *Look Who's Talking*?
   a) Sylvester Stallone
   b) Bruce Willis
   c) Mel Gibson

Answers: 1c, 2b, 3c, 4a, 5b, 6c, 7a, 8a, 9c, 10b

FILM 6

EXPERT

1) What is the name of John Travolta's character in *Saturday Night Fever*?
   a) Danny Zuko
   b) Tony Manero
   c) Vincent Vega

2) What is the significance of the title of the 1960s film *Fahrenheit 451*?
   a) It's the serial number of the last robot made by Dr Fahrenheit
   b) It's the temperature at which paper burns
   c) It's the name of the asteroid on which the action of the film takes place

3) What is unusual about Derek Jarman's 1976 film *Sebastiane*?
   a) It has dialogue in a language invented especially for it
   b) It has only one line of dialogue
   c) Its dialogue is all in Latin

4) Which great painter is portrayed by Kirk Douglas in the 1956 film *Lust for Life*?
   a) Michelangelo
   b) Picasso
   c) Van Gogh

5) Who directed the 1994 movie *Forrest Gump*?
   a) Chris Columbus
   b) Robert Zemeckis
   c) Rob Reiner

6) Which comedian once said that all he needed to make a film was 'a park, a policeman and a pretty girl'?
   a) Charlie Chaplin
   b) Buster Keaton
   c) Woody Allen

7) What was the name of Steven Spielberg's first full-length feature film?
   a) *Jaws*
   b) *The Sugarland Express*
   c) *Duel*

8) From which 1960s film did the band Duran Duran take their name?
   a) *Yellow Submarine*
   b) *Barbarella*
   c) *One Million Years BC*

9) In which film does the mysterious character Keyser Soze feature?
   a) *The Usual Suspects*
   b) *Fargo*
   c) *The Rock*

10) Who directed the 1999 film *American Beauty*?
   a) Sam Mendes
   b) Joel Cohen
   c) Stephen Soderbergh

Answers: 1b, 2b, 3c, 4c, 5b, 6a, 7c, 8b, 9a, 10a

FILM 7

1) In which film does Dustin Hoffman play the character Ray Babbitt?
   a) *Midnight Cowboy*
   b) *Marathon Man*
   c) *Rain Man*

2) Who played Lee Harvey Oswald in the 1991 film *JFK*?
   a) Gary Oldman
   b) Al Pacino
   c) Steve Buscemi

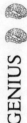

GENIUS

3) *THX 1138* was the first feature film made by which famous director and producer?
   a) Steven Spielberg
   b) George Lucas
   c) Francis Ford Coppola

4) The 1957 Japanese film *Throne of Blood*, directed by Akira Kurosawa, is (loosely) based on which play by Shakespeare?
   a) *King Lear*
   b) *Othello*
   c) *Macbeth*

5) Which Italian film-maker directed the movies *8½* and *Juliet of the Spirits*?
   a) Federico Fellini
   b) Sergio Leone
   c) Michelangelo Antonioni

6) In which American state is the Coen brothers' film *Fargo* set?
   a) Wisconsin
   b) Kansas
   c) Minnesota

7) *The Night of the Hunter*, released in 1955 and starring Robert Mitchum, is the only film directed by which famous British actor?
   a) Lawrence Olivier
   b) Charles Laughton
   c) Richard Burton

GENIUS

8) Which film won Best Picture at the first ever Oscars ceremony in 1927?
   a) *The Jazz Singer*
   b) *All Quiet on the Western Front*
   c) *Wings*

9) Which famous comedian appeared as the Tin Man in a silent version of *The Wizard of Oz*?
   a) Stan Laurel
   b) Oliver Hardy
   c) Buster Keaton

10) Who directed the 1978 version of the film *Invasion of the Body Snatchers*?
   a) Philip Kaufman
   b) Don Siegel
   c) George Miller

Answers: 1c, 2a, 3b, 4c, 5a, 6c, 7b, 8c, 9b, 10a

FILM 8

GENIUS

1) In the 1936 film version of *Romeo and Juliet* who took the title roles?
   a) Douglas Fairbanks Jr and Olivia de Havilland
   b) Lawrence Olivier and Merle Oberon
   c) Leslie Howard and Norma Shearer

2) Which actor made his debut as a director with the 2002 film *Confessions of a Dangerous Mind*?
   a) Gary Oldman
   b) George Clooney
   c) Nicolas Cage

3) Which movie tough guy once remarked that, 'I look like a rock quarry that someone has dynamited'?
   a) Humphrey Bogart
   b) Ernest Borgnine
   c) Charles Bronson

4) What is the name of the character played by Bruce Willis in the *Die Hard* movies?
   a) Martin Riggs
   b) John McClane
   c) Simon Gruber

5) What curious role did Val Kilmer take in the 1993 film *True Romance*?
   a) An alien
   b) The ghost of Elvis Presley
   c) A corpse

6) Who directed the 2000 film thriller *Memento*?
   a) Christopher Nolan
   b) David Fincher
   c) Bryan Singer

7) Which classic Western was based on the magazine story
   The Tin Star by John W. Cunningham?
   a) *The Searchers*
   b) *High Noon*
   c) *Shane*

8) Who played Fleance in Roman Polanski's 1971 film of
   Macbeth?
   a) Keith Chegwin
   b) Jonathan Ross
   c) Shane Richie

9) What role did Harvey Keitel take in Martin Scorsese's film
   The Last Temptation of Christ?
   a) John the Baptist
   b) Judas
   c) Pontius Pilate

10) In which 1940s film did Rita Hayworth sing *Put the Blame
    on Mame*?
    a) *The Lady from Shanghai*
    b) *Cover Girl*
    c) *Gilda*

GENIUS

Answers: 1c, 2b, 3c, 4b, 5b, 6a, 7b, 8a, 9b, 10c

FILM 9

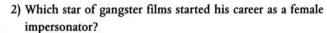

GENIUS

1) Who played Barney Rubble to John Goodman's Fred Flintstone in the 1994 film *The Flintstones*?
   a) Mike Myers
   b) Danny de Vito
   c) Rick Moranis

2) Which star of gangster films started his career as a female impersonator?
   a) Humphrey Bogart
   b) George Raft
   c) James Cagney

3) Who wrote the film scores for both Hitchcock's *North by Northwest* and Scorsese's *Taxi Driver*?
   a) Bernard Herrmann
   b) Henry Mancini
   c) John Barry

4) How many parts did Alec Guinness play in the Ealing black comedy *Kind Hearts and Coronets*?
   a) 6
   b) 8
   c) 10

5) Which British actress appeared, at the age of six, in the 1974 film version of *The Great Gatsby*?
   a) Patsy Kensit
   b) Emma Thompson
   c) Emily Lloyd

6) Who directed the 1994 film *Muriel's Wedding*?
   a) Baz Luhrmann
   b) Stephan Elliott
   c) P. J. Hogan

7) Which Native American actor played Chingachgook in the 1992 film *The Last of the Mohicans*?
   a) Wes Studi
   b) Russell Means
   c) Chief Dan George

8) Who directed Fred Astaire and Ginger Rogers in *Top Hat* and *Shall We Dance*?
   a) Mark Sandrich
   b) Busby Berkeley
   c) Frank Capra

9) Who played Daryl van Horne in the 1987 film *The Witches of Eastwick*?
   a) Warren Beatty
   b) Jack Nicholson
   c) Richard Gere

10) What was the name of Humphrey Bogart's character in the 1948 film *The Treasure of the Sierra Madre*?
   a) Charlie Allnutt
   b) Sam Spade
   c) Fred C. Dobbs

GENIUS

Answers: 1c, 2c, 3a, 4b, 5a, 6c, 7b, 8a, 9b, 10c

HORROR FILMS

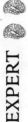

EXPERT

1) What is the name of the character killed in the infamous shower scene in Hitchcock's 1960 film *Psycho*?
   a) Melanie Daniels
   b) Marion Crane
   c) Sarah Arbogast

2) Who directed the 1977 film *Suspiria*?
   a) Dario Argento
   b) Wes Craven
   c) Mario Bava

3) What is the name of the Mummy in the 1999 film *The Mummy*?
   a) Amenhotep
   b) Imhotep
   c) Smenkhare

4) How is Larry Talbot better known in a series of horror films produced by Universal Pictures in the 1940s?
   a) The Wolfman
   b) The Invisible Man
   c) Son of Frankenstein

5) What is the name of the satanic child in the 1976 film *The Omen*?
   a) Dorian
   b) Julian
   c) Damien

6) In which country are victims infected with a 'rage' virus in the film *28 Days Later*?
   a) America
   b) England
   c) Canada

7) Which role did Dwight Frye take in the classic 1930 film version of *Dracula*?
   a) Van Helsing
   b) Renfield
   c) Jonathan Harker

8) Who directed the 1968 film *Night of the Living Dead*?
   a) George A. Romero
   b) Wes Craven
   c) Tobe Hooper

9) On whose novel was the 1973 film *The Exorcist* based?
   a) James Herbert
   b) William P. Blatty
   c) Peter Straub

10) Who played Frankenstein's monster in the 1974 film *Frankenstein and the Monster from Hell*?
   a) Christopher Lee
   b) Bernard Bresslaw
   c) Dave Prowse

EXPERT

Answers: 1b, 2a, 3b, 4a, 5c, 6b, 7b, 8a, 9b, 10c

MOVIE STAR NAMES

Which film stars were originally named:

NOVICE

1) Frances Gumm
   a) Shirley Temple
   b) Bette Davis
   c) Judy Garland

2) Issur Danielovitch
   a) Kirk Douglas
   b) Tony Curtis
   c) Burt Lancaster

3) Thomas Mapother IV
   a) Tom Hanks
   b) Tom Waits
   c) Tom Cruise

4) Spangler Arlington Brugh
   a) Humphrey Bogart
   b) Robert Taylor
   c) Ray Milland

5) Betty Joan Perske
   a) Doris Day
   b) Lauren Bacall
   c) Elizabeth Taylor

6) **Camille Javal**
   a) Brigitte Bardot
   b) Catherine Deneuve
   c) Jeanne Moreau

7) **Caryn Johnson**
   a) Whoopi Goldberg
   b) Demi Moore
   c) Halle Berry

8) **William Franklin Beedle Jr**
   a) Joseph Cotten
   b) William Holden
   c) Charlton Heston

9) **William Henry Pratt**
   a) Boris Karloff
   b) Edward G. Robinson
   c) James Cagney

10) **Margaret Mary Emily Anne Hyra**
   a) Demi Moore
   b) Nicole Kidman
   c) Meg Ryan

NOVICE

Answers: 1c, 2a, 3c, 4b, 5b, 6a, 7a, 8b, 9a, 10c

OSCARS

1) Which film won the Best Picture award at the 1998 Oscars?
   a) *Saving Private Ryan*
   b) *Titanic*
   c) *Shakespeare in Love*

2) Which of the following directors is yet to win an Oscar?
   a) Oliver Stone
   b) Steven Spielberg
   c) Martin Scorsese

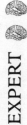

3) How many Oscars did David Lean's film *Lawrence of Arabia* win in the 1962 Awards?
   a) 5
   b) 7
   c) 12

4) In 1969 who won the Oscar for Best Supporting Actor for his role in *They Shoot Horses, Don't They*?
   a) Ed Begley
   b) Martin Balsam
   c) Gig Young

5) Who is the oldest person to win the Oscar for Best Actress?
   a) Jessica Tandy for *Driving Miss Daisy*
   b) Katherine Hepburn for *On Golden Pond*
   c) Marie Dressler for *Min and Bill*

6) In 1941 which movie beat *Citizen Kane* and *The Maltese Falcon* to take the Oscar for Best Picture?
   a) *How Green Was My Valley*
   b) *The Little Foxes*
   c) *Sergeant York*

7) Which of the following performers won an Oscar for *Bonnie and Clyde* in 1967?
   a) Faye Dunaway
   b) Gene Hackman
   c) Estelle Parsons

8) Which of the following singers has been nominated for a Best Actress Oscar?
   a) Diana Ross
   b) Whitney Houston
   c) Madonna

9) Which actor was nominated for the Best Actor Oscar for four consecutive years between 1951 and 1954?
   a) Humphrey Bogart
   b) Marlon Brando
   c) Gregory Peck

10) Who won the Oscar for Best Director in 1996 for *The English Patient*?
   a) Anthony Minghella
   b) Sam Mendes
   c) Barry Levinson

Answers: 1c, 2c, 3b, 4c, 5a, 6a, 7c, 8a, 9b, 10a

RADIO

1) Which BBC Radio 1 DJ married Fatboy Slim?
   a) Annie Nightingale
   b) Sara Cox
   c) Zoe Ball

2) In which year did *The Archers* begin broadcasting?
   a) 1949
   b) 1951
   c) 1953

EXPERT

3) Which journalist and broadcaster presented the long-running BBC Radio series *Letter from America*?
   a) Alastair Cooke
   b) Roy Plomley
   c) John Humphrys

4) What was the original name of *The Goon Show*?
   a) *It's A Mad World*
   b) *Crazy People*
   c) *Loons at Large*

5) On which radio station did Chris Tarrant present the breakfast show for 17 years?
   a) Radio 1
   b) Virgin FM
   c) Capital FM

6) In 1938 who broadcast a radio adaptation of H. G. Wells's
The War of the Worlds which persuaded millions of
Americans that Martians had landed on Earth?
a) Orson Welles
b) Alfred Hitchcock
c) Cecil B. de Mille

7) Which radio programme is introduced by the music *Sailing
By* by Ronald Binge?
a) *Desert Island Discs*
b) *The Late Night Shipping Forecast*
c) *Woman's Hour*

8) Which classic radio comedy show included the characters
Rambling Syd Rumpo, Binky Huckaback and Dame Celia
Molestrangler?
a) *I'm Sorry, I'll Read That Again*
b) *ITMA*
c) *Round the Horne*

9) What is the real name of Mark Radcliffe's radio sidekick, Lard?
a) Marc Riley
b) Chris Moyles
c) Matthew Bannister

10) In what year did Classic FM begin broadcasting?
a) 1991
b) 1992
c) 1993

Answers: 1c, 2b, 3a, 4b, 5c, 6a, 7b, 8c, 9a, 10b

TELEVISION CHARACTERS

In which TV series do or did the following characters appear?

1) Kochanski
   a) *MASH*
   b) *This Life*
   c) *Red Dwarf*

2) Nurse Emmanuel
   a) *Open All Hours*
   b) *Casualty*
   c) *E. R.*

3) Tinker Deal
   a) *The Darling Buds of May*
   b) *Bergerac*
   c) *Lovejoy*

4) Maddy Magellan
   a) *Jonathan Creek*
   b) *Bewitched*
   c) *Father Ted*

5) Frank Furillo
   a) *NYPD Blue*
   b) *Hill Street Blues*
   c) *Kojak*

EXPERT

6) Granny Clampett
- a) *The Beverley Hillbillies*
- b) *The Addams Family*
- c) *The Dukes of Hazzard*

7) John Cage
- a) *Friends*
- b) *Sex and the City*
- c) *Ally McBeal*

8) Wesley Pegden
- a) *Heartbeat*
- b) *The Last of the Summer Wine*
- c) *On the Buses*

EXPERT

9) Professor John Robinson
- a) *Lost in Space*
- b) *Mission Impossible*
- c) *Space 1999*

10) Steve Keller
- a) *Rawhide*
- b) *The Streets of San Francisco*
- c) *The Naked City*

Answers: 1c, 2a, 3c, 4a, 5b, 6a, 7c, 8b, 9a, 10b

TELEVISION COMEDY

NOVICE

1) In *Hancock's Half-Hour*, where did Tony Hancock live?
   a) The Laurels, Brickfield Terrace, Holloway
   b) 42 Viaduct Way, Ruislip
   c) 23 Railway Cuttings, East Cheam

2) What was the name of Steptoe Senior in *Steptoe and Son*?
   a) Arthur
   b) Albert
   c) Alfred

3) In which county is *Last of the Summer Wine* set?
   a) Yorkshire
   b) Lancashire
   c) Devon

4) What is the surname of Del Boy and Rodney in *Only Fools and Horses*?
   a) Potter
   b) Trotter
   c) Blotter

5) What was the setting for *Drop the Dead Donkey*?
   a) A newspaper office
   b) A bookmaker's
   c) A works canteen

6) Which scriptwriter created the sitcoms *The Liver Birds* and *Bread*?
   a) John Sullivan
   b) Phil Redmond
   c) Carla Lane

7) In which American sitcom does David Hyde Pierce play the central character's prissy brother?
   a) *Frasier*
   b) *The Fresh Prince of Bel Air*
   c) *Seinfeld*

8) The characters in which American comedy show of the 1970s and 1980s appeared originally in a novel by Richard Hooker?
   a) *MASH*
   b) *Cheers*
   c) *Soap*

NOVICE

9) In which classic American sitcom did characters called Lurch, Pugsley and Fester appear?
   a) *The Munsters*
   b) *The Beverley Hillbillies*
   c) *The Addams Family*

10) Who plays Chandler in *Friends*?
   a) Matthew Perry
   b) Matt LeBlanc
   c) David Schwimmer

Answers: 1c, 2b, 3a, 4b, 5a, 6c, 7a, 8a, 9c, 10a

TELEVISION 1

NOVICE

1) In which city is *Taggart* set?
   a) Newcastle
   b) London
   c) Glasgow

2) Which TV comedian used the catchphrase, 'Ooh, you are awful. But I like you.'?
   a) Tommy Cooper
   b) Dick Emery
   c) Eric Morecambe

3) Who provided the voice for Bob the Builder?
   a) Neil Morrissey
   b) Martin Clunes
   c) Rik Mayall

4) In which American city was the comedy series *Cheers* set?
   a) New York
   b) Seattle
   c) Boston

5) In what year did BBC2 begin broadcasting?
   a) 1962
   b) 1964
   c) 1966

6) Who replaced Magnus Magnusson as the question-master on *Mastermind*?
   a) Jeremy Paxman
   b) John Humphrys
   c) Michael Aspel

7) Who played Tara King in *The Avengers*?
   a) Linda Thorson
   b) Diana Rigg
   c) Honor Blackman

8) From which series was *Knots Landing* a spin-off?
   a) *Dynasty*
   b) *Hawaii Five-0*
   c) *Dallas*

9) Which of the Teletubbies is green?
   a) Dipsy
   b) Tinky-Winky
   c) Laa-Laa

10) Which long-running British TV series was first shown on the day after the assassination of John F. Kennedy?
   a) *Panorama*
   b) *Doctor Who*
   c) *Blue Peter*

NOVICE

Answers: 1c, 2b, 3a, 4c, 5b, 6b, 7a, 8c, 9a, 10b

TELEVISION 2

NOVICE

1) In which fictional Yorkshire village is *Heartbeat* set?
   a) Aidensfield
   b) Wetherfield
   c) Walford

2) In *Dad's Army* what was Private Fraser's occupation?
   a) Butcher
   b) Undertaker
   c) Chemist

3) Which king was played by Keith Michell in a 1970 TV series?
   a) Henry VIII
   b) Charles II
   c) Henry V

4) On which US programme was *University Challenge* based?
   a) Ivy League Challenge
   b) Rose Bowl Challenge
   c) College Bowl

5) Who was the first host of *Blankety Blank* when it began in 1979?
   a) Les Dawson
   b) Terry Wogan
   c) Bruce Forsyth

6) Who plays Gil Grissom in the American crime series *CSI*?
   a) David Caruso
   b) Michael Douglas
   c) William Petersen

7) Who played the lead role in *Kavanagh QC*?
   a) John Nettles
   b) John Snow
   c) John Thaw

8) In which decade was Parliament first televised?
   a) 1970s
   b) 1980s
   c) 1990s

9) What is the name of Edina's daughter in *Absolutely Fabulous*?
   a) Posy
   b) Saffron
   c) Bluebell

10) What is the name of the TV and film production company founded by Prince Edward?
   a) Ardent
   b) Argent
   c) Urgent

NOVICE

Answers: 1a, 2b, 3a, 4c, 5b, 6c, 7c, 8b, 9b, 10a

TELEVISION 3

1) Which fictional city is the setting for *Coronation Street*?
   a) Lanchester
   b) Weatherfield
   c) Grantchester

2) In the 1970s American cop series *Starsky and Hutch* who played Hutch?
   a) Paul Michael Glaser
   b) David Soul
   c) David Janssen

3) For what company did Reggie Perrin work in *The Rise and Fall of Reginald Perrin*?
   a) Sunshine Foods
   b) Sunshine Chocolates
   c) Sunshine Desserts

4) Which British TV drama featured characters called Warren, Milly, Miles and Egg?
   a) *This Life*
   b) *Our Friends in the North*
   c) *Casualty*

5) Which TV comedy series was largely set in a small town called Royston Vasey?
   a) *The Office*
   b) *Fawlty Towers*
   c) *The League of Gentlemen*

6) Who was the first Doctor Who?
   a) Patrick Troughton
   b) William Hartnell
   c) Peter Cushing

7) In *The Magic Roundabout* what sort of animal was Dylan?
   a) Dog
   b) Cat
   c) Rabbit

8) In 1958 who were the presenters of the very first edition of the children's programme *Blue Peter*?
   a) Christopher Trace and Leila Williams
   b) Christopher Trace and Valerie Singleton
   c) Valerie Singleton and John Noakes

9) Which TV police series began life as a single, one-off drama called *Woodentop*?
   a) *Softly, Softly*
   b) *The Bill*
   c) *Mersey Beat*

10) In *The X-Files,* what was Mulder's first name?
   a) Fox
   b) Wolf
   c) Dane

NOVICE

Answers: 1b, 2b, 3c, 4a, 5c, 6b, 7c, 8a, 9b, 10a

TELEVISION 4

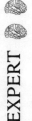

EXPERT

1) Which writer created the character of Jonathan Creek?
   a) Simon Nye
   b) David Renwick
   c) Andrew Davies

2) Who replaced Patrick Troughton as Doctor Who?
   a) Tom Baker
   b) Jon Pertwee
   c) Sylvester McCoy

3) In which TV series did Charles Dance play Guy Perron?
   a) *Brideshead Revisited*
   b) *The Jewel in the Crown*
   c) *Fortunes of War*

4) What was the name of the slave played by Frankie Howerd in *Up Pompeii?*
   a) Lurcio
   b) Sarcio
   c) Burcio

5) Which TV series is set in the fictional village of Lochdubh?
   a) *Hamish Macbeth*
   b) *Monarch of the Glen*
   c) *The Irish RM*

6) What was the name of the hospital in the series
   St. Elsewhere?
   a) St. James
   b) St. Elmo
   c) St. Elgius

7) In which TV crime series did Chief Inspector Haskins
   appear?
   a) *The Professionals*
   b) *Softly, Softly*
   c) *The Sweeney*

8) What is the name of the central character in *Prime Suspect?*
   a) Samantha Ryan
   b) Jane Tennison
   c) Lynda La Plante

9) Who replaced Richard Baker as the presenter of the proms
   on BBC TV?
   a) Valerie Singleton
   b) John Humphrys
   c) James Naughtie

10) In which sitcom did the characters 'Bootsie' and 'Snudge'
    first appear?
    a) *The Army Game*
    b) *The Rag Trade*
    c) *On the Buses*

EXPERT

Answers: 1b, 2b, 3b, 4a, 5a, 6c, 7c, 8b, 9c, 10a

TELEVISION 5

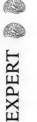

EXPERT

1) Which British police series took its central character from a 1949 film called *The Blue Lamp*?
   a) *Z-Cars*
   b) *Dixon of Dock Green*
   c) *Softly, Softly*

2) Who was the female presenter on *TISWAS*?
   a) Sarah Greene
   b) Tina Heath
   c) Sally James

3) Who played Catweazle in the 1970s series of that name?
   a) Geoffrey Palmer
   b) Geoffrey Bayldon
   c) Geoffrey Bailey

4) Who created and narrated the American cult series *The Twilight Zone*?
   a) Aaron Spelling
   b) Rod Serling
   c) Quinn Martin

5) In which American city is *Columbo* set?
   a) New York
   b) San Francisco
   c) Los Angeles

6) Who played Hoss Cartwright in *Bonanza*?
   a) Lorne Greene
   b) Michael Landon
   c) Dan Blocker

7) *A. J. Wentworth BA* was the final starring vehicle for which late and much-loved comedy actor?
   a) Jimmy Edwards
   b) Arthur Lowe
   c) Frankie Howerd

8) What is the surname of Buffy the Vampire Slayer?
   a) Summers
   b) Spring
   c) Winters

EXPERT

9) Who created *Rutland Weekend Television*?
   a) John Cleese
   b) Eric Idle
   c) Michael Palin

10) Which actor is married to the *Sex and the City* star Sarah Jessica Parker?
   a) Russell Crowe
   b) Matthew Modine
   c) Matthew Broderick

Answers: 1b, 2c, 3b, 4b, 5c, 6c, 7b, 8a, 9b, 10c

TELEVISION 6

1) Which TV couple lived in Lanford, Illinois?
   a) Roseanne and Dan Conner
   b) Lucille Ball and Desi Arnaz
   c) Dr Huxtable and Clair Huxtable

2) On which long-running series is Carenza Lewis a resident expert?
   a) *Antiques Roadshow*
   b) *Time Team*
   c) *The Sky at Night*

3) Who played Danny McGlone in the 1987 series *Tutti Frutti*?
   a) Robert Carlyle
   b) Billy Connolly
   c) Robbie Coltrane

4) Which soap was originally to be called *One Way Street*?
   a) *Brookside*
   b) *Home and Away*
   c) *Neighbours*

5) Who played Richard III in an episode of *Blackadder*?
   a) Rik Mayall
   b) Peter Cook
   c) Spike Milligan

GENIUS

6) In which fictitious small town was '*Allo* '*Allo* set?
   a) Plouvion
   b) Nouvion
   c) Souvion

7) What was Captain Mainwaring's first name in *Dad's Army*?
   a) George
   b) Arthur
   c) Alfred

8) Which TV talk show hostess co-starred with Divine in John Waters's 1988 film *Hairspray*?
   a) Vanessa Feltz
   b) Oprah Winfrey
   c) Ricki Lake

9) Which future Oscar winner played Irma Ogden's boyfriend in *Coronation Street*?
   a) Patrick Stewart
   b) Ben Kingsley
   c) Ian McShane

10) Which TV family live at 1313 Mockingbird Heights?
   a) The Waltons
   b) The Simpsons
   c) The Munsters

GENIUS

Answers: 1a, 2b, 3c, 4c, 5b, 6b, 7a, 8c, 9b, 10c

TELEVISION 7

GENIUS

1) Which British TV and film actress is married to the Hollywood director Taylor Hackford?
a) Helen Mirren
b) Joanna Lumley
c) Amanda Burton

2) Who played the Emperor Nero in the 1976 series *I, Claudius*?
a) Derek Jacobi
b) Christopher Biggins
c) John Hurt

3) Which classic sitcom began as a one-off thirty-minute show called *The Offer*?
a) *Dad's Army*
b) *Steptoe and Son*
c) *The Likely Lads*

4) What was the name of the character played by David Jason in *Porridge*?
a) Blanco
b) Bunco
c) Danko

5) On which TV series did Maureen Reece come to the nation's attention?
a) *The Cruise*
b) *Driving School*
c) *Airport*

6) Who was the first presenter of *Changing Rooms*?
   a) Linda Barker
   b) Lawrence Llewellyn-Bowen
   c) Carol Smillie

7) Which London suburb was the setting for *Citizen Smith*?
   a) Balham
   b) Wimbledon
   c) Tooting

8) Who conducted the first British TV interview with Nelson Mandela after his release from prison in 1990?
   a) Jeremy Paxman
   b) Trevor McDonald
   c) Robin Day

9) Which TV play by Dennis Potter has its child characters played by adult actors?
   a) *Cold Lazarus*
   b) *Cream in my Coffee*
   c) *Blue Remembered Hills*

10) In *In Sickness and in Health* what was the name of the character who looked after Alf Garnett after his wife died?
    a) Mrs Hollingberry
    b) Mrs Hollinghurst
    c) Mrs Boysenberry

GENIUS

Answers: 1a, 2b, 3b, 4a, 5b, 6c, 7c, 8b, 9c, 10a

TELEVISION SOAPS 1

EXPERT

1) In *Coronation Street*, for what was Deirdre Rachid imprisoned?
   a) Murder
   b) Fraud
   c) Theft

2) In *Emmerdale*, which character arranged his suicide to make it look as though his wife had murdered him?
   a) Chris Tate
   b) Cain Dingle
   c) Eric Pollard

3) Which soap's introductory music is *Barwick Green* from the suite *My Native Heath*, written in 1924 by the Yorkshire composer Arthur Wood?
   a) *Coronation Street*
   b) *The Archers*
   c) *Hollyoaks*

4) When was the final episode of the Liverpool-based soap *Brookside* screened?
   a) August 2001
   b) September 2002
   c) November 2003

5) Where is the soap *Hollyoaks* set?
   a) Liverpool
   b) Chester
   c) Warrington

6) In *Neighbours*, Max Hoyland has two children from his first marriage. What are their names?
a) Sky and Serena
b) Flick and Connor
c) Boyd and Summer

7) What character did Dannii Minogue play in *Home and Away*?
a) Pippa
b) Emma
c) Ailsa

8) Which soap opera was voted 11th in the Channel 4 programme *The 100 Greatest TV Moments from Hell*?
a) *Triangle*
b) *Howard's Way*
c) *Eldorado*

EXPERT

9) In *Eastenders*, who shot Phil Mitchell in 2001?
a) Grant Mitchell
b) Lisa Shaw
c) Dot Cotton

10) In 1965 which well-known playwright wrote five episodes for *Mrs Dale's Diary*, the first post-war soap on British radio?
a) Tom Stoppard
b) Harold Pinter
c) John Osborne

Answers: 1b, 2a, 3b, 4c, 5b, 6c, 7b, 8c, 9b, 10a

TELEVISION SOAPS 2

GENIUS

1) In *Dynasty* which character was played by Rock Hudson?
   a) Lucas Carter
   b) Daniel Reece
   c) Zach Powers

2) Barry Crocker sings the theme song for which Australian soap?
   a) *Heartbreak High*
   b) *Home and Away*
   c) *Neighbours*

3) What happened to Reg Cox in the very first episode of *Eastenders*?
   a) He was married
   b) He was killed
   c) His house burned down

4) In what London postal district is Walford?
   a) E20
   b) E17
   c) E18

5) Which of the following was a name originally intended to be given to *Coronation Street*?
   a) Northern Echoes
   b) Victoria Road
   c) Florizel Street

6) Who played Frank Tate in *Emmerdale*?
   a) Norman Bowler
   b) Frederick Pyne
   c) Frazer Hines

7) In *Coronation Street* what was Alf Roberts's occupation before he ran the corner shop?
   a) Policeman
   b) Plumber
   c) Postman

8) What was the name of the song performed by *Emmerdale* cast members which entered the charts in 1997?
   a) *Hillbilly Rock*
   b) *The Woolpack Anthem*
   c) *Emmerdale Forever*

9) In which soap is there a character called Sky Mangel?
   a) *Home and Away*
   b) *Neighbours*
   c) *Heartbreak High*

10) Who played Beth Jordache in *Brookside*?
   a) Anna Friel
   b) Claire Sweeney
   c) Alexandra Fletcher

Answers: 1b, 2c, 3b, 4a, 5c, 6a, 7c, 8a, 9b, 10a

WESTERNS

EXPERT

1) Who played Shane in the 1953 film of that name?
   a) James Stewart
   b) Randolph Scott
   c) Alan Ladd

2) Who played Little Bill Daggett in the 1992 Clint Eastwood movie *Unforgiven*?
   a) Gene Hackman
   b) Richard Harris
   c) Morgan Freeman

3) Which Native American tribe featured in the 1990 Kevin Costner western *Dances with Wolves*?
   a) Sioux
   b) Apache
   c) Cheyenne

4) Which legendary Western star appeared as one of the Three Mesquiteers in a series of 1930s B-movies?
   a) Randolph Scott
   b) James Stewart
   c) John Wayne

5) Who directed the classic 1959 Western *Rio Bravo*?
   a) John Ford
   b) Howard Hawks
   c) George Stevens

6) Which legendary character does Richard Mulligan play in the 1970 film *Little Big Man*?
   a) Wild Bill Hickok
   b) General Custer
   c) Jesse James

7) Which former child star appeared in a Western called *Fort Apache* in 1948?
   a) Jackie Cooper
   b) Jackie Coogan
   c) Shirley Temple

8) What was the name of the 1994 Western which starred Mel Gibson and Jodie Foster?
   a) *Maverick*
   b) *American Outlaws*
   c) *Palomino*

EXPERT

9) Who played Doc Holliday to Kurt Russell's Wyatt Earp in the 1993 film *Tombstone*?
   a) William Hurt
   b) Val Kilmer
   c) Jeff Bridges

10) For what are the outlaws searching in Sergio Leone's 1966 film *The Good, the Bad and the Ugly*?
   a) Buried cash
   b) The man who killed their partner
   c) A goldmine

Answers: 1c, 2a, 3a, 4c, 5b, 6b, 7c, 8a, 9b, 10a

GENERAL KNOWLEDGE

CAR REGISTRATION

Which countries use the following letters as their international car registration?

EXPERT

1) E
   a) Spain
   b) Ecuador
   c) Eritrea

2) N
   a) Netherlands
   b) Nigeria
   c) Norway

3) K
   a) Korea
   b) Kenya
   c) Cambodia

4) RA
   a) Argentina
   b) Romania
   c) Rwanda

5) S
   a) Singapore
   b) Sweden
   c) Switzerland

6) C

a) Canada
b) Colombia
c) Cuba

7) FL

a) Liechtenstein
b) Luxembourg
c) Liberia

8) MOC

a) Morocco
b) Mozambique
c) Monaco

EXPERT

9) ZA

a) Zambia
b) South Africa
c) Zimbabwe

10) DZ

a) Algeria
b) Germany
c) Tanzania

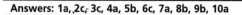

Answers: 1a, 2c, 3c, 4a, 5b, 6c, 7a, 8b, 9b, 10a

COLOURS

NOVICE

1) Which colour takes its name from a nineteenth century battle fought between the French and the Austrians?
   a) Indigo
   b) Magenta
   c) Sepia

2) Which colour was first used to describe a synthetic dye created by British chemist William Perkin in 1856?
   a) Mauve
   b) Purple
   c) Indigo

3) Who painted the picture most commonly known as *The Blue Boy*?
   a) Joshua Reynolds
   b) Thomas Gainsborough
   c) William Hogarth

4) Of which legendary rock band was Syd Barrett once a member?
   a) Deep Purple
   b) Black Sabbath
   c) Pink Floyd

5) What type of creature is a Clouded Yellow?
   a) Moth
   b) Dragonfly
   c) Butterfly

6) What is Orange Pekoe?
   a) A tea
   b) A variety of pineapple
   c) A liqueur

7) Which author created the character of the Scarlet Pimpernel?
   a) Arthur Conan Doyle
   b) Baroness Orczy
   c) John Buchan

NOVICE

8) Which of the following is a shade of brown?
   a) Sepia
   b) Magenta
   c) Veridian

9) In Ancient Rome what colour was considered the symbol of imperial power?
   a) Crimson
   b) Purple
   c) Yellow

10) Which Shakespearean heroine spoke of her 'salad days when I was green in judgement'?
    a) Lady Macbeth
    b) Cleopatra
    c) Juliet

Answers: 1b, 2a, 3b, 4c, 5c, 6a, 7b, 8a, 9b, 10b

FOOD AND DRINK 1

NOVICE

1) Apart from potato, what is the principal vegetable in vichyssoise soup?
   a) Leek
   b) Onion
   c) Asparagus

2) What do the initials V.S.O.P. stand for on a bottle of brandy?
   a) Very Special Old Pale
   b) Very Special Over Proof
   c) Veritas Semper Omnia Plaudit

3) What is a chorizo?
   a) A Spanish salad vegetable
   b) A Spanish smoked sausage
   c) A Spanish meat stew

4) If food is described as 'impanato', what does this mean?
   a) Breaded
   b) Boiled
   c) Baked

5) What do the French call custard?
   a) Crème anglais
   b) Crème brulée
   c) Coutarde

6) Which salad vegetable is the main ingredient in the Greek dish tzatziki?
   a) Tomato
   b) Cucumber
   c) Lettuce

7) Roquefort cheese is made from the milk of which animal?
   a) Sheep
   b) Goat
   c) Cow

8) What are the principal ingredients of a Waldorf salad?
   a) Apples, carrots and mayonnaise
   b) Apples, celery and walnuts
   c) Apples, cheese and grapes

NOVICE

9) Which vegetable did Mark Twain describe as 'nothing but a cabbage with a college education'?
   a) Broccoli
   b) Lettuce
   c) Cauliflower

10) From which American state does Jack Daniel's Whiskey come?
   a) Texas
   b) Tennessee
   c) Louisiana

Answers: 1a, 2a, 3b, 4a, 5a, 6b, 7a, 8b, 9c, 10b

FOOD AND DRINK 2

NOVICE

1) What type of food is Bombay Duck?
   a) A pâté
   b) A dried fish
   c) Duck in a curry sauce

2) What are the two main components of a Horse's Neck?
   a) Gin and white wine
   b) Vodka and tomato juice
   c) Brandy and ginger ale

3) Which ingredient would you expect to find in a dish described as 'forestière'?
   a) Mushrooms
   b) Venison
   c) Strawberries

4) In which country would you be most likely to be offered Vegemite to eat?
   a) USA
   b) Jamaica
   c) Australia

5) What is the literal meaning of 'vermicelli'?
   a) Green pasta
   b) Little worms
   c) Heavenly rice

6) Jersey Royal, Wilja and Maris Piper are all varieties of which foodstuff?
   a) Potatoes
   b) Apples
   c) Lettuces

7) From which language does the word 'chutney' come?
   a) Hindi
   b) Urdu
   c) Japanese

8) Which sauce takes its name from a 17th century French financier at the court of Louis XIV?
   a) Béarnaise
   b) Mornay
   c) Béchamel

NOVICE

9) Where was Worcestershire sauce invented?
   a) England
   b) Australia
   c) India

10) What is the principal ingredient of couscous?
   a) Wheat
   b) Beans
   c) Rice

Answers: 1b, 2c, 3a, 4c, 5b, 6a, 7a, 8c, 9c, 10a

143

GARDENS AND GARDENERS

1) Who was the first presenter of the BBC programme
   Gardening Club which began in 1956?
   a) Geoff Hamilton
   b) Percy Thrower
   c) Clay Jones

2) The gardens of Versailles are chiefly the work of which
   French landscape designer?
   a) André Le Nôtre
   b) Jean-Baptiste Alexandre le Blond
   c) André Mollet

GENIUS

3) Which of the following gardeners and broadcasters was a
   member of the first *Gardeners' Question Time* panel in 1947?
   a) Professor Alan Gemmell
   b) Bill Sowerbutts
   c) Bob Flowerdew

4) Which of the following gardens, designed by Vita
   Sackville-West, can be seen at Sissinghurst Castle in Kent?
   a) The Knot Garden
   b) The Sunken Garden
   c) The White Garden

5) What was "Capability" Brown's real first name?
   a) Percival
   b) Lancelot
   c) Arthur

6) Who assisted Gertrude Jekyll in the design and planting of many of her famous gardens?
   a) Sir Edwin Lutyens
   b) Vita Sackville-West
   c) Charles Rennie Mackintosh

7) With which historic house was Joseph Paxton, gardener, garden designer and architect, closely associated for most of his working life?
   a) Knole House
   b) Chatsworth House
   c) Hatfield House

GENIUS

8) Which famous diarist was also a designer of gardens?
   a) John Evelyn
   b) Samuel Pepys
   c) Henry "Chips" Channon

9) The mother of which king was responsible for the founding of Kew Gardens in 1759?
   a) George II
   b) George III
   c) George IV

10) "Oh, Adam was a gardener, and God who made him sees/That half a proper gardener's work is done upon his knees". Which writer claimed Adam as the first gardener?
   a) John Betjeman
   b) Robert Browning
   c) Rudyard Kipling

Answers: 1b, 2a, 3b, 4c, 5b, 6a, 7b, 8a, 9b, 10c

GENERAL KNOWLEDGE 1

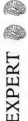

EXPERT

1) Where can you find the Drakensberg range of mountains?
   a) Europe
   b) Australia
   c) Africa

2) In the TV series *Frasier*, what type of dog is Martin Crane's pet Eddie?
   a) An Alsatian
   b) A Jack Russell Terrier
   c) A Cocker Spaniel

3) Which method of movement to music was developed by Emile Jacques-Dalcroze?
   a) Callisthenics
   b) Eurhythmics
   c) Kinesthetics

4) What is the capital of Canada's Yukon territory?
   a) Yellowknife
   b) Whitehorse
   c) Charlottetown

5) Which make of car was advertised with the slogan, 'Vorsprung Durch Technik'?
   a) Mercedes
   b) Audi
   c) Volkswagen

6) What name was shared by the second and sixth US presidents?
   a) Adams
   b) Jackson
   c) Jefferson

7) What is an appaloosa?
   a) A striped wild cat
   b) A spotted riding horse
   c) A flying lizard

8) Which animal did G. K. Chesterton describe in a poem as 'the devil's walking parody on all four-footed things'?
   a) The giraffe
   b) The camel
   c) The donkey

9) On which Mediterranean island can the megalithic temple of Hagar Qim be found?
   a) Cyprus
   b) Malta
   c) Rhodes

10) Which Victorian artist painted *The Light of the World*?
   a) John Everett Millais
   b) Edwin Landseer
   c) William Holman Hunt

Answers: 1c, 2b, 3b, 4b, 5b, 6a, 7b, 8c, 9b, 10c

GENERAL KNOWLEDGE 2

1) Which river flows through the Grand Canyon, Arizona?
   a) Rio Grande
   b) Colorado
   c) Platte River

2) What is an onager?
   a) A wild ass
   b) A type of finch
   c) A freshwater alligator

NOVICE

3) What is the correct term for the flat-topped funerary structures which surround the Pyramids of Giza?
   a) Mastabas
   b) Pediments
   c) Ziggurats

4) Which battle in the Napoleonic Wars is sometimes known as 'the Battle of the Three Emperors'?
   a) Waterloo
   b) Jena
   c) Austerlitz

5) From the wood of which tree was Noah's Ark built?
   a) Oak
   b) Cedar
   c) Gopher

6) Of which group of islands is Hugh Town the capital?
   a) Channel Islands
   b) Isles of Scilly
   c) Shetland Isles

7) How many standard bottles of champagne make up a Balthazar?
   a) 12
   b) 16
   c) 24

8) What do you use to play the game 'craps'?
   a) Cards
   b) Dominoes
   c) Dice

NOVICE

9) Which marshal in Napoleon's armies became King Charles XIV of Sweden and Norway?
   a) Michel Ney
   b) Joachim Murat
   c) Jean-Baptiste Bernadotte

10) Which English city was called Eboracum by the Romans?
   a) Chester
   b) St. Albans
   c) York

Answers: 1b, 2a, 3a, 4c, 5c, 6b, 7b, 8c, 9c, 10c

GENERAL KNOWLEDGE 3

1) **On which river does Limerick stand?**
   a) The Shannon
   b) The Liffey
   c) The Barrow

2) **Who wrote the Mary Poppins stories?**
   a) Dodie Smith
   b) Joyce Lankester Brisley
   c) P. L. Travers

EXPERT

3) **Which London hospital was founded in 1721 by a philanthropic printer and bookseller?**
   a) The Royal Marsden Hospital
   b) The Maudsley Hospital
   c) Guy's Hospital

4) **Which German composer wrote the opera *Hansel and Gretel*, first performed in 1893?**
   a) Richard Strauss
   b) Engelbert Humperdinck
   c) Richard Wagner

5) **In Greek mythology who was the son of Odysseus and Penelope?**
   a) Telemachus
   b) Orestes
   c) Hippolytus

6) What is the name of the Norwegian parliament?
   a) The Stortinget
   b) The Knesset
   c) The Althingi

7) Which Duke's eldest son has the title the Marquis of Blandford?
   a) Duke of Bedford
   b) Duke of Westminster
   c) Duke of Marlborough

EXPERT

8) What common word is officially defined as 1/100th of a second?
   a) A tick
   b) A trice
   c) A jiffy

9) In which South American country does the Atacama Desert lie?
   a) Peru
   b) Chile
   c) Argentina

10) Which fictional character was imprisoned in the Chateau D'If?
   a) The Scarlet Pimpernel
   b) The Count of Monte Cristo
   c) The Barber of Seville

Answers: 1a, 2c, 3c, 4b, 5a, 6a, 7c, 8c, 9b, 10b

GENERAL KNOWLEDGE 4

1) When is Thanksgiving Day celebrated in the US?
a) The second Thursday in November
b) The third Thursday in November
c) The fourth Thursday in November

2) Which planet do the Daleks in *Doctor Who* call home?
a) Durko
b) Pharos
c) Skaro

3) In which ship did Captain Scott sail on his last expedition to the Antarctic?
a) *The Terra Nova*
b) *The Discovery*
c) *The Endurance*

4) Which fictional character lived in the village of Puddleby-on-the-Marsh?
a) Dr Dolittle
b) Willy Wonka
c) Miss Marple

5) Which well-known operetta has the subsidiary title *The Slave of Duty*?
a) *Orpheus in the Underworld* by Offenbach
b) *Die Fledermaus* by Johann Strauss
c) *The Pirates of Penzance* by Gilbert and Sullivan

EXPERT

6) In the New Testament who was chosen as an apostle to take the place of Judas Iscariot?
   a) Matthias
   b) Thomas
   c) Zacharias

7) Which queen of the English is believed never to have set foot in England?
   a) Henrietta Maria
   b) Eleanor of Aquitaine
   c) Berengaria

EXPERT

8) Who was the first woman to swim the English Channel?
   a) Amy Johnson
   b) Gertrude Ederle
   c) Sonja Henie

9) Which drink is named after the London barman who invented it in the 1840s?
   a) Pimms
   b) Harvey Wallbanger
   c) Tom Collins

10) In which year did the battle of Flodden Field take place?
   a) 1314
   b) 1415
   c) 1513

Answers: 1c, 2c, 3a, 4a, 5c, 6a, 7c, 8b, 9a, 10c

GENERAL KNOWLEDGE 5

1) Which golfer was nicknamed 'The Golden Bear'?
   a) Arnold Palmer
   b) Jack Nicklaus
   c) Lee Trevino

2) In which English county can you find the Whipsnade Wild Animal Park?
   a) Bedfordshire
   b) Essex
   c) Surrey

NOVICE

3) Which two books of the Bible were reputedly written by a physician?
   a) Luke and Acts
   b) John and Mark
   c) Matthew and Luke

4) Which annual festival was once called Samhain?
   a) Hallowe'en
   b) St. Valentine's Day
   c) New Year's Day

5) Which is the world's smallest independent state?
   a) Monaco
   b) San Marino
   c) Vatican City

6) Who was the President of the Confederate States of America at the time of the American Civil War?
   a) Robert E. Lee
   b) Jefferson Davis
   c) Ulysses S. Grant

7) Which London monument now stands on the original site of the gallows at Tyburn?
   a) Admiralty Arch
   b) Marble Arch
   c) Nelson's Column

8) After how many years of marriage do you celebrate your tin wedding anniversary?
   a) 5
   b) 10
   c) 15

9) Which of the following is not a true nut?
   a) Peanut
   b) Chestnut
   c) Hazelnut

10) Which British king was married at one time to Maria Anne Fitzherbert?
   a) George IV
   b) George III
   c) Charles II

NOVICE

Answers: 1b, 2a, 3a, 4a, 5c, 6b, 7b, 8b, 9a, 10a

GENERAL KNOWLEDGE 6

1) What is the name of the island in New York harbour on which the Statue of Liberty stands?
   a) Ellis Island
   b) Harbour Island
   c) Bedloe's Island

2) Which league was formed in 1839 under the leadership of Richard Cobden and John Bright?
   a) The Electoral Reform League
   b) The Anti-Corn Law League
   c) The League of Gentlemen

3) Which London prison, formerly situated in Southwark, is described by Dickens in *Little Dorrit*?
   a) The Marshalsea
   b) Newgate
   c) The Clink

4) What was the name of the missionary to China who was portrayed by Ingrid Bergman in the 1958 film *The Inn of the Sixth Happiness*?
   a) Gladys Aylward
   b) Helen Keller
   c) Mary Slessor

5) In which British city can Haymarket and Waverley railway stations be found?
   a) Leeds
   b) Manchester
   c) Edinburgh

6) From what plant is saffron obtained?

 a) Poppy

 b) Crocus

 c) Aconite

7) In the film *Good Will Hunting*, who played Will Hunting?

 a) Robin Williams

 b) Ben Affleck

 c) Matt Damon

8) What was the name of the police officer in the cartoon series *Top Cat*?

 a) Officer Drabble

 b) Officer Dibble

 c) Officer Dumble

EXPERT

9) Who was King of England at the time of the Great Fire of London?

 a) Charles I

 b) Charles II

 c) James II

10) What was the name of Desmond Dekker's backing group on the 1960s hit *The Israelites*?

 a) The Aces

 b) The Deuces

 c) The Jokers

Answers: 1c, 2b, 3a, 4a, 5c, 6b, 7c, 8b, 9b, 10a

GENERAL KNOWLEDGE 7

1) How many sides does a 50p coin have?
   a) 6
   b) 7
   c) 8

2) What was the name of Don Quixote's horse?
   a) Rosalind
   b) Perdita
   c) Rosinante

3) In *Monopoly* which street joins Bow Street and Marlborough Street to complete a set?
   a) Bond Street
   b) Coventry Street
   c) Vine Street

4) How many lines of verse are there in a sonnet?
   a) 12
   b) 14
   c) 24

5) In which town is Fenner's cricket ground?
   a) Cambridge
   b) Canterbury
   c) Oxford

NOVICE

6) Who played Sebastian Flyte in the TV series *Brideshead Revisited*?
   a) Jeremy Irons
   b) Anthony Andrews
   c) Lawrence Olivier

7) Which musical includes the song *Oh what a beautiful mornin'*?
   a) *Carousel*
   b) *Oklahoma!*
   c) *South Pacific*

8) In the animal world, what is a monotreme?
   a) A mammal that rears its young in a pouch
   b) A mammal that lays eggs
   c) A mammal with webbed feet

9) How could you come across the fictional English county of Borsetshire?
   a) By reading the novels of Anthony Trollope
   b) By tuning into *The Archers*
   c) By playing the board game *Cluedo*

10) Who was the first member of the royal family to be interviewed on TV?
   a) George VI
   b) The Queen
   c) Prince Philip

NOVICE

Answers: 1b, 2c, 3c, 4b, 5a, 6b, 7b, 8b, 9b, 10c

GENERAL KNOWLEDGE 8

EXPERT

1) What does the word Zorro mean in Spanish?
   a) Fox
   b) Sword
   c) Avenger

2) In which English public school is the game of squash said to have originated?
   a) Eton College
   b) Harrow
   c) Marlborough

3) Who was British Prime Minister when Edward VIII abdicated in 1936?
   a) Winston Churchill
   b) Neville Chamberlain
   c) Stanley Baldwin

4) In Stanley Kubrick's film *2001: A Space Odyssey*, what song does the computer HAL sing?
   a) *Hey Jude*
   b) *Home, Sweet Home*
   c) *Daisy, Daisy (A Bicycle Built for Two)*

5) Which empire dominated Central America in the 15th century AD?
   a) The Mayan Empire
   b) The Inca Empire
   c) The Aztec Empire

6) What was The Clash's only No. 1 single?
   a) *Rock the Casbah*
   b) *Should I Stay Or Should I Go?*
   c) *London Calling*

7) What breed of dog is Snoopy in the strip cartoon *Peanuts*?
   a) Beagle
   b) Basset Hound
   c) Dachshund

8) The Simplon Tunnel runs through which range of mountains?
   a) The Dolomites
   b) The Alps
   c) The Pyrenees

9) Which make of car featured in the film *Back to the Future*?
   a) Volkswagen Beetle
   b) Ford Mustang
   c) De Lorean

10) In which year did *Eastenders* first appear on our TV screens?
   a) 1983
   b) 1985
   c) 1987

EXPERT

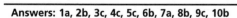

Answers: 1a, 2b, 3c, 4c, 5c, 6b, 7a, 8b, 9c, 10b

GENERAL KNOWLEDGE 9

NOVICE

1) How is Beethoven's *Symphony no. 3 in E Flat Minor* better known?
   a) The 'Pastoral'
   b) The 'Eroica'
   c) The 'Choral'

2) What position did Lee Kuan Yew hold from 1959 to 1990?
   a) President of South Korea
   b) Prime Minister of Singapore
   c) Secretary General of the United Nations

3) Who plays Martin Platt in *Coronation Street*?
   a) William Roache
   b) Jack Shepherd
   c) Sean Wilson

4) What nationality was the explorer Abel Tasman?
   a) Portuguese
   b) Dutch
   c) Swedish

5) What is a wampee?
   a) A root vegetable
   b) A flowering shrub
   c) A fruit

6) What is the name of Captain Ahab's ship in Herman Melville's novel *Moby Dick*?
   a) Rachel
   b) Hispaniola
   c) Pequod

7) Where is the British National Railway Museum?
   a) Darlington
   b) Stockton-on-Tees
   c) York

8) What is the second book of the Bible?
   a) Exodus
   b) Numbers
   c) Deuteronomy

9) Which 1970s pop group included the Longmuir brothers, Derek and Alan?
   a) Mud
   b) The Bay City Rollers
   c) The Rubettes

10) Who played Jack Ryan in the 1992 film version of Tom Clancy's novel *Patriot Games*?
   a) Gene Hackman
   b) Sean Connery
   c) Harrison Ford

NOVICE

Answers: 1b, 2b, 3c, 4b, 5c, 6c, 7c, 8a, 9b, 10c

GENERAL KNOWLEDGE 10

1) **What is the inscription on the Victoria Cross?**
   a) For valour
   b) For courage
   c) For heroism

2) **What 1760s invention by John Spilsbury became a popular pastime?**
   a) The jigsaw puzzle
   b) The frisbee
   c) The yo-yo

3) **For which area of the British Isles did Alfred Wainwright write a series of famous guidebooks?**
   a) The Lake District
   b) The Pennines
   c) The Scottish Highlands

4) **Which is the longest passenger liner ever built?**
   a) The *Queen Elizabeth II*
   b) The *Titanic*
   c) The *Queen Mary II*

5) **What is the flavouring in ouzo?**
   a) Bergamot
   b) Aniseed
   c) Peppermint

EXPERT

6) What is a fox's den called?
   a) An earth
   b) A holt
   c) A lair

7) Which organisation was founded by the Reverend Chad Varah?
   a) Christian Aid
   b) The Samaritans
   c) Oxfam

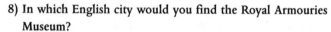

8) In which English city would you find the Royal Armouries Museum?
   a) Leeds
   b) Manchester
   c) London

EXPERT

9) In which gangster film did Al Pacino star as Tony Montana?
   a) *Scarface*
   b) *Goodfellas*
   c) *Donnie Brasco*

10) Who is the only female winner of the Perrier Comedy Award?
   a) Dawn French
   b) Jo Brand
   c) Jenny Eclair

Answers: 1a, 2a, 3a, 4c, 5b, 6a, 7b, 8a, 9a, 10c

GENERAL KNOWLEDGE 11

NOVICE

1) Of which Native American tribe was Geronimo a leader?
   a) Sioux
   b) Cherokee
   c) Apache

2) In which year did the £1 note cease to be legal tender in Britain?
   a) 1986
   b) 1988
   c) 1990

3) According to the *Highway Code*, at what age is a passenger responsible for ensuring that he/she wears a seatbelt?
   a) 12
   b) 14
   c) 16

4) Which member of Tony Blair's government has been nicknamed 'Two Jags'?
   a) David Blunkett
   b) John Prescott
   c) Gordon Brown

5) Which British yachtswoman hit the headlines when she came second in the 2000 Vendee Globe Round the World Yacht Race?
   a) Ellen MacArthur
   b) Clare Francis
   c) Emma Richards

6) Which of these road tunnels does not run underneath the Thames?
   a) Dartford
   b) Baldock
   c) Blackwall

7) Who was Dan Dare's evil enemy?
   a) Lex Luthor
   b) Emperor Ming the Merciless
   c) The Mekon

8) Which James Bond theme song was written by Paul McCartney?
   a) *Live and Let Die*
   b) *The Living Daylights*
   c) *You Only Live Twice*

9) A cete is the name for a group of which British animals?
   a) Pine Martens
   b) Otters
   c) Badgers

10) Who directed the 1998 British gangster film *Lock, Stock and Two Smoking Barrels*?
   a) Danny Boyle
   b) Guy Ritchie
   c) Mike Figgis

NOVICE

Answers: 1c, 2b, 3b, 4b, 5a, 6b, 7c, 8a, 9c, 10b

GENERAL KNOWLEDGE 12

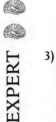

EXPERT

1) What is a kakapo?
   a) A beetle
   b) A flightless parrot
   c) A Hawaiian fish dish

2) Of which famous ship was Benjamin Briggs the captain?
   a) *Titanic*
   b) *Mary Celeste*
   c) *Lusitania*

3) In which TV sketch show did characters called Swiss Toni, Bob Fleming and Competitive Dad appear?
   a) *Dead Ringers*
   b) *Smack the Pony*
   c) *The Fast Show*

4) Which American state has its capital at Helena?
   a) Montana
   b) Wisconsin
   c) Idaho

5) In heraldry what colour is described as 'gules'?
   a) Red
   b) Blue
   c) Gold

6) Who wrote the song *Trains and Boats and Planes*?
   a) Lennon and McCartney
   b) Sammy Cahn
   c) Burt Bacharach

7) What sort of animal is a Clydesdale?
   a) Horse
   b) Cow
   c) Pig

8) Who plays Judge John Deed in the BBC TV drama of that name?
   a) Trevor Eve
   b) Martin Shaw
   c) Alan Davies

9) How many of the Channel Tunnel's 31 miles are under water?
   a) 17
   b) 23
   c) 29

10) How many legs does a spider have?
   a) Six
   b) Eight
   c) Ten

EXPERT

Answers: 1b, 2b, 3c, 4a, 5a, 6c, 7a, 8b, 9b, 10b

GENERAL KNOWLEDGE 13

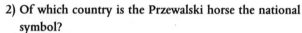

1) Which adventurer, born in Barnstaple, Devon, in 1901, sailed around the world alone in a 55-foot sailing yacht?
   a) Sir Alec Rose
   b) Sir Francis Chichester
   c) Sir Robin Knox-Johnston

2) Of which country is the Przewalski horse the national symbol?
   a) Poland
   b) Mongolia
   c) Kyrgyzstan

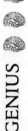

GENIUS

3) Which car company has a model called the Rabbit?
   a) Saab
   b) Volvo
   c) Volkswagen

4) In which country would you find the ethnic group known as Burakumin?
   a) China
   b) Japan
   c) South Korea

5) Which herb is *Salvia officinalis*?
   a) Sage
   b) Rue
   c) Thyme

6) Which famous annual sporting event did Miguel Indurain win every year from 1991 to 1995?
   a) The Indianapolis 500
   b) The Tour de France
   c) The US Golf Masters

7) Who was the Roman emperor at the time of the birth of Christ?
   a) Augustus
   b) Tiberius
   c) Nero

8) What was REM's first UK top ten hit?
   a) *Stand*
   b) *Shiny Happy People*
   c) *Everybody Hurts*

9) Whom did Sir Alex Ferguson succeed as manager of Manchester United in 1986?
   a) Ron Atkinson
   b) Tommy Docherty
   c) Dave Sexton

10) What was the route of the original Orient Express in the 1920s?
   a) Paris to Venice
   b) Paris to Istanbul
   c) Paris to Brindisi

Answers: 1b, 2b, 3c, 4b, 5a, 6b, 7a, 8b, 9a, 10b

GENERAL KNOWLEDGE 14

1) Which British ship, launched in February 1906, gave its name to a new class of battleships?
   a) HMS *Dreadnought*
   b) HMS *Invincible*
   c) HMS *Indomitable*

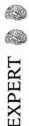

2) What is the national bird of Sweden?
   a) White Stork
   b) European Robin
   c) Eurasian Blackbird

EXPERT

3) Who was the author of the books about Thomas the Tank Engine?
   a) The Reverend W. Awdry
   b) Enid Blyton
   c) Roger Dean

4) What is the name of the Queen of Spain?
   a) Sofia
   b) Maria
   c) Caroline

5) In which British town or city is there a Bridge of Sighs?
   a) York
   b) Bath
   c) Cambridge

6) In which sport would you perform a 'randolph'?
   a) Figure skating
   b) Trampolining
   c) Diving

7) Where did the first FA Cup final take place?
   a) Kennington Oval
   b) White City
   c) Wembley

8) Which vegetable has varieties called 'globe' and 'Jerusalem'?
   a) Artichoke
   b) Cabbage
   c) Broad bean

9) What was Disney's second animated feature film?
   a) *Dumbo*
   b) *Pinocchio*
   c) *Fantasia*

10) In bridge how many tricks make up a grand slam?
   a) 5
   b) 7
   c) 13

EXPERT

Answers: 1a, 2c, 3a, 4a, 5c, 6b, 7a, 8a, 9b, 10c

GENERAL KNOWLEDGE 15

1) With which innovation in marine transport is the 17th century Dutchman Cornelius van Drebbel most associated?
   a) The first iron ship
   b) The first steamship
   c) The first submarine

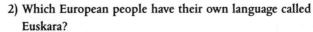

2) Which European people have their own language called Euskara?
   a) The Basques
   b) The Catalans
   c) The Galicians

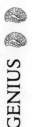

GENIUS

3) In which country was the first Hyundai car built?
   a) Japan
   b) South Korea
   c) Taiwan

4) Which order of insects are known to scientists as coleoptera?
   a) Moths
   b) Beetles
   c) Butterflies

5) Which famous horse race was won in three successive years in the 1960s by *Arkle*?
   a) The Cheltenham Gold Cup
   b) The Derby
   c) The St. Leger

6) In which American TV series is one of the central characters called Mitch Buchannon?
   a) *Dynasty*
   b) *Hawaii 5-0*
   c) *Baywatch*

7) Which Roman goddess was the equivalent of Artemis, the Greek goddess of hunting?
   a) Ceres
   b) Diana
   c) Venus

8) Which US President authorised the dropping of the atomic bombs on Hiroshima and Nagasaki?
   a) Eisenhower
   b) Roosevelt
   c) Truman

9) Which English poet had the middle name of Chawner?
   a) Siegfried Sassoon
   b) Rupert Brooke
   c) Wilfred Owen

10) In what year was the British railway system privatised?
   a) 1991
   b) 1994
   c) 1996

Answers: 1c, 2a, 3b, 4b, 5a, 6c, 7b, 8c, 9b, 10b

GENERAL KNOWLEDGE 16

1) Of which railway company was Isambard Kingdom Brunel
the chief engineer in the mid-19th century?
   a) GNER
   b) LNER
   c) GWR

2) Which parts of the rhubarb are poisonous?
   a) the stems
   b) the leaves
   c) the flowers

3) Where is Nelson buried?
   a) All Saints Church, Burnham Thorpe, Norfolk
   b) Westminster Abbey
   c) St. Paul's Cathedral

4) In which Shakespearean play do two characters called
Gobbo appear?
   a) *Measure for Measure*
   b) *The Merchant of Venice*
   c) *All's Well That Ends Well*

5) What did Elisha Otis invent in 1853?
   a) The lift
   b) The moving staircase
   c) The dumb waiter

6) In which 1960s group was Judith Durham a singer?
   a) Manfred Mann
   b) Procul Harum
   c) The Seekers

7) Who directed the films *Midnight Cowboy* and *Marathon Man*?
   a) Mike Nichols
   b) John Schlesinger
   c) Tony Richardson

8) The *Mary Rose* was the flagship of which English king?
   a) Henry VII
   b) Henry VIII
   c) Charles II

GENIUS

9) What name is given to the six administrative divisions of the Isle of Man?
   a) Ridings
   b) Sheadings
   c) Boroughs

10) What is a nilgai?
    a) An Indian antelope
    b) An African buffalo
    c) An African bird

Answers: 1c, 2b, 3c, 4b, 5a, 6c, 7b, 8b, 9b, 10a

HOW MANY?

How many of the following are/were there?

NOVICE

1) Wonders of the Ancient World
   a) Five
   b) Seven
   c) Nine

2) Kings of France named Louis
   a) Sixteen
   b) Seventeen
   c) Eighteen

3) Popes named Pius
   a) Eleven
   b) Twelve
   c) Thirteen

4) Ways to leave your lover in a Paul Simon song
   a) Thirty
   b) Forty
   c) Fifty

5) Lords a-leaping in *The Twelve Days of Christmas*
   a) Nine
   b) Ten
   c) Twelve

6) Time Zones
   a) Twenty-four
   b) Twenty-six
   c) Thirty

7) Steps in a novel by John Buchan
   a) Twenty-nine
   b) Thirty-nine
   c) Forty-nine

8) Books in the New Testament
   a) Twenty-seven
   b) Thirty-nine
   c) Forty-one

9) Furlongs in a mile
   a) Six
   b) Eight
   c) Ten

10) Russian Tsars named Nicholas
   a) Two
   b) Three
   c) Four

NOVICE

Answers: 1b, 2c, 3b, 4c, 5b, 6a, 7b, 8a, 9b, 10a

PHOBIAS

If you suffer from the following phobias, what do you fear?

1) **Gynophobia**
   a) Pregnancy
   b) Women
   c) Sex

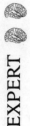

2) **Triskaidekaphobia**
   a) Dreaming
   b) Long words
   c) The number thirteen

EXPERT

3) **Bufonophobia**
   a) Frogs
   b) Spiders
   c) Toads

4) **Tachophobia**
   a) Speed
   b) Light
   c) Darkness

5) **Pogonophobia**
   a) Beards
   b) Thunder
   c) Cats

6) Ergophobia
- a) Idleness
- b) Work
- c) Drugs

7) Suriphobia
- a) Mice
- b) Rats
- c) Worms

8) Selenophobia
- a) The Sun
- b) The stars
- c) The Moon

EXPERT

9) Kleptophobia
- a) Walking
- b) Sleeping
- c) Stealing

10) Homichlophobia
- a) Little green men
- b) Fog
- c) Smoke

Answers: 1b, 2c, 3c, 4a, 5a, 6b, 7a, 8c, 9c, 10b

TRAINS, BOATS AND PLANES

1) **Where was the *Titanic* built?**
   a) Belfast
   b) Glasgow
   c) Southampton

EXPERT

2) **The first passenger-carrying railway in the world opened in 1825. Between which two towns did it run?**
   a) Stockton and Darlington
   b) Manchester and Liverpool
   c) Darlington and Liverpool

3) **In which English town would you find a sculpture called *Train* which was unveiled in 1997?**
   a) Darlington
   b) York
   c) Manchester

4) **Which English city has its own dedicated Train Operating Company?**
   a) Hull
   b) Manchester
   c) Bristol

5) **Who designed the giant flying boat that was nicknamed the Spruce Goose?**
   a) Charles Lindbergh
   b) Barnes Wallis
   c) Howard Hughes

6) Which section of line was the first to be opened on the London Underground in 1863?
   a) Between Paddington and Kensington
   b) Between Farringdon and Moorgate
   c) Between Paddington and Farringdon

7) Aeroflot is the national airline of which country?
   a) Greece
   b) Russia
   c) Finland

8) Which aircraft company first produced the Second World War bomber plane, the *Halifax*?
   a) Handley Page
   b) De Havilland
   c) Avro

9) Where would you find the longest stretch of straight railroad track in the world?
   a) The Trans-Siberian Railway, on the route from Moscow to Irkutsk
   b) In Australia, on the route from Sydney to Perth across the Nullarbor Plain
   c) The Alamosa-Salida section in Colorado, USA

10) On which ship did Napoleon surrender to the British in 1815?
   a) HMS *Victory*
   b) HMS *Temeraire*
   c) HMS *Bellerophon*

Answers: 1a, 2a, 3a, 4a, 5c, 6c, 7b, 8a, 9b, 10c

GEOGRAPHY

AFRICA

1) What is the largest country in Africa?
   a) Algeria
   b) Angola
   c) Sudan

2) Where in Africa are the Victoria Falls?
   a) Lake Victoria
   b) The River Nile
   c) The River Zambezi

3) What is the capital of Malawi?
   a) Lilongwe
   b) Kinshasa
   c) Kigali

4) Of which European country was Mozambique once a colony?
   a) France
   b) Portugal
   c) Great Britain

5) What is the name of the African city once known as Salisbury?
   a) Kampala
   b) Ouagadougou
   c) Harare

EXPERT

6) In West Africa what is a 'griot'?
   a) a storyteller
   b) a type of antelope
   c) a small hill

7) Which of the following countries is entirely surrounded by South Africa?
   a) Namibia
   b) Lesotho
   c) Angola

EXPERT

8) Which African country was founded in 1847 by freed American slaves?
   a) Libya
   b) Liberia
   c) Burkina Faso

9) Which African country was once known as 'The Gold Coast'?
   a) Ghana
   b) Benin
   c) Sierra Leone

10) In which African country are the Ruwenzori Mountains?
   a) Sudan
   b) Nigeria
   c) Uganda

Answers: 1c, 2c, 3a, 4b, 5c, 6a, 7b, 8b, 9a, 10c

THE AMERICAS

NOVICE

1) What is the capital city of Canada?
   a) Ottawa
   b) Quebec
   c) Toronto

2) Which are the only two landlocked countries in South America?
   a) Bolivia and Uruguay
   b) Paraguay and Bolivia
   c) Venezuela and Bolivia

3) Which state of the USA lies between Lake Michigan and Lake Huron?
   a) Colorado
   b) Wisconsin
   c) Michigan

4) Easter Island, with its mysterious statues, belongs to which South American country?
   a) Argentina
   b) Chile
   c) Peru

5) In which American state is the Grand Canyon?
   a) Colorado
   b) New Mexico
   c) Arizona

6) In which South American country are the Angel Falls, the longest free fall of water in the world?
   a) Venezuela
   b) Suriname
   c) Brazil

7) How many stripes are there on the flag of the USA?
   a) 13
   b) 20
   c) 50

8) What bird features on the flag of Mexico?
   a) A condor
   b) An eagle
   c) A hummingbird

9) Which state of the USA has its capital in Springfield?
   a) Illinois
   b) Iowa
   c) Idaho

10) As well as its ten provinces, Canada has other self-governing regions known as Territories. Which of the following is a Canadian Territory?
   a) Quebec
   b) Prince Edward Island
   c) The Yukon

NOVICE

Answers: 1a, 2b, 3c, 4b, 5c, 6a, 7a, 8b, 9a, 10c

ASIA

1) Who was the founder and first president of North Korea?
   a) Kim Il-Song
   b) Kim Chong-Il
   c) Paek Nam Sun

2) In which Chinese city is the Bund, a collection of early 20th century neo-classical European buildings?
   a) Taipei
   b) Shanghai
   c) Beijing

GENIUS

3) Which country's capital is Thimphu?
   a) Nepal
   b) Kyrgyzstan
   c) Bhutan

4) Of which European country was Macau once a colony?
   a) Portugal
   b) France
   c) The Netherlands

5) What are the official languages of India?
   a) Urdu and Hindi
   b) Hindi and English
   c) Urdu and English

6) Which four countries border Pakistan?
   a) Iran, Afghanistan, India and China
   b) Afghanistan, India, Turkmenistan, China
   c) Iran, India, Uzbekistan, Afghanistan

7) In which modern country is the ancient city of Samarkand?
   a) Uzbekistan
   b) Kyrgyzstan
   c) Kazakhstan

8) Which is Japan's largest island?
   a) Hokkaido
   b) Kyushu
   c) Honshu

9) Which strait separates China from Taiwan?
   a) The China Strait
   b) The Hong Strait
   c) The Taiwan Strait

10) In which country would you find the Gobi Desert?
   a) China
   b) North Korea
   c) Mongolia

GENIUS

Answers: 1a, 2b, 3c, 4a, 5b, 6a, 7a, 8c, 9c, 10c

AUSTRALIA

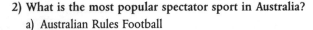

1) **What is the capital city of Australia?**
   a) Sydney
   b) Canberra
   c) Melbourne

2) **What is the most popular spectator sport in Australia?**
   a) Australian Rules Football
   b) Rugby
   c) Cricket

GENIUS

3) **Which day in the year is Australia Day?**
   a) July 26th
   b) June 26th
   c) January 26th

4) **In which area of Australia would you find Kakadu National Park?**
   a) The Northern Territory
   b) Western Australia
   c) New South Wales

5) **In which year were the last convicts shipped from Britain to Australia?**
   a) 1858
   b) 1868
   c) 1878

6) Through which Australian city does the River Swan flow?
   a) Perth
   b) Brisbane
   c) Melbourne

7) What is the name of the Australian national anthem?
   a) Waltzing Matilda
   b) Australia, 'Tis of Thee
   c) Advance Australia Fair

8) In which year were the Olympic Games held in the Australian city of Melbourne?
   a) 1956
   b) 1948
   c) 1932

9) What is the aboriginal name of Ayers Rock?
   a) Uhuru
   b) Uluru
   c) Toowoomba

10) In Australia what is a bunyip?
   a) A legendary creature
   b) A bushman's blanket
   c) A type of tree

GENIUS

Answers: 1b, 2a, 3c, 4a, 5b, 6a, 7c, 8a, 9b, 10a

BRIDGES

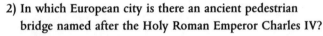

1) Which bridge was designed by Benjamin Baker and Sir John Fowler and opened in 1890 by the Prince of Wales?
   a) The Golden Gate Bridge, San Francisco
   b) The Sydney Harbour Bridge
   c) The Forth Rail Bridge, Scotland

2) In which European city is there an ancient pedestrian bridge named after the Holy Roman Emperor Charles IV?
   a) Prague
   b) Rome
   c) Vienna

3) Which bridge over the Seine in Paris is a footbridge only?
   a) Pont du Neuf
   b) Pont des Arts
   c) Pont Henri IV

4) Under which London bridge was the Italian banker Roberto Calvi found hanging in 1982?
   a) London Bridge
   b) Blackfriars Bridge
   c) Tower Bridge

5) Which bridge, opened in 2000, connects the Danish capital Copenhagen with the Swedish mainland?
   a) Øresund Bridge
   b) Queen Christina Bridge
   c) Skagerrak Bridge

GENIUS

6) **What is the Pont du Gard at Nimes in France?**
   a) A bridge with battlements, guarding a palace
   b) A Roman aqueduct
   c) The oldest packhorse bridge in France

7) **Which river in New York does the Brooklyn Bridge span?**
   a) West River
   b) South River
   c) East River

8) **Which bridge was captured by British Commandos on the 5th June 1944?**
   a) Arnhem
   b) Pegasus
   c) The bridge on the River Kwai

9) **What is the name of the modern ten-mile bridge crossing the Tagus River in Portugal?**
   a) The Vasco de Gama Bridge
   b) Prince Henry the Navigator Bridge
   c) Magellan Bridge

10) **Where is the world's first iron bridge, completed in 1779?**
   a) Coalbrookdale, England
   b) Cardiff, Wales
   c) Paisley, Glasgow, Scotland

GENIUS

Answers: 1c, 2a, 3b, 4b, 5a, 6b, 7c, 8b, 9a, 10a

BUILDINGS

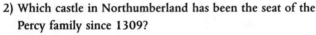
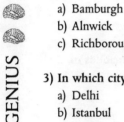

GENIUS

1) Which artist is buried in the Pantheon in Rome?
   a) Raphael
   b) Michelangelo
   c) Leonardo da Vinci

2) Which castle in Northumberland has been the seat of the Percy family since 1309?
   a) Bamburgh
   b) Alnwick
   c) Richborough

3) In which city can you find the Topkapi Palace?
   a) Delhi
   b) Istanbul
   c) Beijing

4) Marble Arch was built originally as the entrance to which building?
   a) St. James's Palace
   b) The Tower of London
   c) Buckingham Palace

5) In which country would you find the fortress of Paramonga?
   a) Peru
   b) Mexico
   c) Brazil

6) Which is the largest inhabited castle in the British Isles?
   a) Edinburgh
   b) Windsor
   c) Inveraray

7) Who is the architect of the new Jewish Museum in Berlin?
   a) Norman Foster
   b) Daniel Libeskind
   c) Rem Koolhaas

8) What was the original purpose of the building in Paris that now houses the Musée d'Orsay?
   a) A prison
   b) A railway station
   c) A royal palace

GENIUS

9) In which country is the Shwe Dagon Pagoda?
   a) Cambodia
   b) Myanmar
   c) Laos

10) Which New York skyscraper, designed by William van Alen, stands at 405 Lexington Avenue between 42nd and 43rd Street?
   a) The Empire State Building
   b) The Rockefeller Centre
   c) The Chrysler Building

Answers: 1a, 2b, 3b, 4c, 5a, 6b, 7b, 8b, 9b, 10c

ENGLAND 1

NOVICE

1) Which range of hills is often referred to as 'the backbone of England'?
   a) The Chilterns
   b) The Cheviots
   c) The Pennines

2) In which English county is Tewkesbury?
   a) Shropshire
   b) Gloucestershire
   c) Herefordshire

3) Of which English city is Armley a suburb?
   a) Leeds
   b) Manchester
   c) Birmingham

4) What is the county town of Northumberland?
   a) Morpeth
   b) Alnwick
   c) Hexham

5) Which motorway runs between Birmingham and Exeter?
   a) M4
   b) M5
   c) M6

6) A man born in the county of Kent is called either 'a Kentish man' or 'a man of Kent' but what determines which term is used?
   a) Which side of the River Medway he was born
   b) Whether a man was born on the Kent Weald or not
   c) Whether or not he was born on the Isle of Sheppey

7) Which river provides much of the border between Devon and Cornwall?
   a) Exe
   b) Tamar
   c) Avon

8) Which Suffolk town is home to an annual music festival?
   a) Ipswich
   b) Felixstowe
   c) Aldeburgh

9) In which county is the botanical site known as the Eden Project?
   a) Cornwall
   b) Devon
   c) Somerset

10) In which county is the Beamish open-air industrial museum?
   a) Warwickshire
   b) Durham
   c) West Yorkshire

NOVICE

Answers: 1c, 2b, 3a, 4a, 5b, 6a, 7b, 8c, 9a, 10b

ENGLAND 2

1) Which is the longest lake in England?
   a) Windermere
   b) Ullswater
   c) Ness

2) Which town on the south coast became a city as part of the Millennium celebrations?
   a) Plymouth
   b) Bournemouth
   c) Brighton

3) In which county is St. Michael's Mount to be found?
   a) Cornwall
   b) Devon
   c) Somerset

4) The Isle of Sheppey is part of which county?
   a) Dorset
   b) Kent
   c) Sussex

5) Which English city is associated with the legend of Lady Godiva?
   a) Coventry
   b) Gloucester
   c) Chester

NOVICE

6) In which county is Blue John mined?
   a) Cheshire
   b) Derbyshire
   c) Lancashire

7) Which town in North Yorkshire is famous for its annual bed race?
   a) Knaresborough
   b) Pickering
   c) Whitby

8) With which seafood is Whitstable associated?
   a) Whitebait
   b) Shrimps
   c) Oysters

9) In which county is the Forest of Dean?
   a) Gloucestershire
   b) Warwickshire
   c) Kent

10) In which English town is there a street called The Pantiles?
   a) Ipswich
   b) Tunbridge Wells
   c) Chester

NOVICE

Answers: 1a, 2c, 3a, 4b, 5a, 6b, 7a, 8c, 9a, 10b

ENGLISH CITIES

NOVICE

1) Which of these English cities is famous for the manufacture of lace?
   a) Nottingham
   b) Doncaster
   c) Lincoln

2) In which city can you visit John Wesley's Chapel, the world's first Methodist Chapel, where he used to preach?
   a) Manchester
   b) Bristol
   c) Leicester

3) In which city are gates called 'bars' and streets called 'gates'?
   a) Liverpool
   b) Bath
   c) York

4) Which city houses the National Exhibition Centre?
   a) London
   b) Birmingham
   c) Sheffield

5) Which of these museums can be visited at Gloucester docks?
   a) The National Maritime Museum
   b) The National Waterways Museum
   c) The Boat Museum

6) Which city was the birthplace of the poet and playwright Christopher Marlowe?
   a) Canterbury
   b) Rochester
   c) Norwich

7) Through which of the following cities does the River Wye flow?
   a) Gloucester
   b) Hereford
   c) Chichester

8) Which city was the setting for the film *The Full Monty*?
   a) Liverpool
   b) Manchester
   c) Sheffield

9) Which city houses the National Museum of Photography, Film & Television?
   a) London
   b) Bradford
   c) Birmingham

10) Of which university city is St. Frideswide the patron saint?
    a) Cambridge
    b) Durham
    c) Oxford

NOVICE

Answers: 1a, 2b, 3c, 4b, 5b, 6a, 7b, 8c, 9c, 10c

EUROPE

EXPERT

1) In which country is the city of Kaunas?
   a) Lithuania
   b) Latvia
   c) Estonia

2) Which two colours appear on the Swedish national flag?
   a) Red and white
   b) Blue and yellow
   c) Blue and white

3) Which of the following islands is one of the Aeolian Islands?
   a) Naxos
   b) Stromboli
   c) Elba

4) What is the capital of Albania?
   a) Sarajevo
   b) Skopje
   c) Tirana

5) In which of the following countries is the euro not the unit of currency?
   a) Greece
   b) Norway
   c) Finland

6) Which of the following cities does not stand on the river Danube?
   a) Bucharest
   b) Belgrade
   c) Budapest

7) Which is the longest river in France?
   a) Rhone
   b) Seine
   c) Loire

8) Which European city was once known as Ragusa?
   a) Vienna
   b) Trieste
   c) Dubrovnik

9) In which country is Romansch one of four official languages?
   a) Switzerland
   b) Italy
   c) Croatia

10) In which European city can you find a park called the Prater?
   a) Berlin
   b) Vienna
   c) Prague

EXPERT

Answers: 1a, 2b, 3b, 4c, 5b, 6a, 7c, 8c, 9a, 10b

LAKES & RIVERS

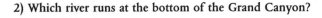

GENIUS

1) **How is the Bodensee better known in English?**
   a) Lake Constance
   b) Lake Lucerne
   c) Lake Garda

2) **Which river runs at the bottom of the Grand Canyon?**
   a) Rio Grande
   b) Snake
   c) Colorado

3) **Which lake is the source of the White Nile?**
   a) Lake Chad
   b) Lake Victoria
   c) Lake Tanganyika

4) **What is the highest waterfall in the United States?**
   a) Niagara Falls
   b) Sentinel Falls
   c) Yosemite Falls

5) **In which country is the Murray-Darling river to be found?**
   a) Scotland
   b) Australia
   c) South Africa

6) Into which body of water does the River Ganges empty?
   a) The Bay of Bengal
   b) The Indian Ocean
   c) The Coral Sea

7) Which is the largest freshwater lake (in area) in the British Isles?
   a) Loch Ness
   b) Lake Windermere
   c) Lough Neagh

8) In which country is the world's largest man-made lake?
   a) China
   b) Uganda
   c) Egypt

9) On which river does the German city of Hamburg stand?
   a) The Elbe
   b) The Rhine
   c) The Spee

10) Which is the longest river in Canada?
   a) Niagara
   b) St. Lawrence
   c) Mackenzie

GENIUS

Answers: 1a, 2c, 3b, 4c, 5b, 6a, 7c, 8b, 9a, 10c

LONDON

EXPERT

1) In which street did the Great Fire of London start in 1666?
   a) Fleet Street
   b) Pudding Lane
   c) Poultry

2) In which London square are there statues of both Winston Churchill and Abraham Lincoln?
   a) Trafalgar Square
   b) St. John's Square
   c) Parliament Square

3) Which London church is known as 'The Actors' Church' because of its long association with theatrical people?
   a) St. Anne's, Soho
   b) St. Martin-in-the-Fields
   c) St. Paul's, Covent Garden

4) Which famous London building was reputedly built by Henry I's jester, Rahere?
   a) Westminster Abbey
   b) St. Bartholomew's Hospital
   c) The Tower of London

5) Which of the following underground lines does not have a station at Edgware Road?
   a) Bakerloo
   b) Northern
   c) District

6) In which London park is Speaker's Corner?
   a) Hyde Park
   b) Green Park
   c) Regent's Park

7) Which new London landmark was designed by David Marks and Julia Barfield?
   a) Millennium Bridge
   b) London Eye
   c) Millennium Dome

EXPERT

8) In which London museum is the Henry Cole Wing?
   a) British Museum
   b) Natural History Museum
   c) Victoria and Albert Museum

9) Which of the following tube stations takes its name from a pub that used to be on the site?
   a) Angel
   b) Royal Oak
   c) Barbican

10) Which famous fictional character is commemorated by a statue in Kensington Gardens?
   a) Sherlock Holmes
   b) Mr Pickwick
   c) Peter Pan

Answers: 1b, 2c, 3c, 4b, 5b, 6a, 7b, 8c, 9a, 10c

MAN-MADE WONDERS

In which modern country can the following man-made wonders of the world be found?

GENIUS

1) The Temple of Angkor Wat
   a) Myanmar
   b) Cambodia
   c) Vietnam

2) The ruined city of Machu Picchu
   a) Mexico
   b) Guatemala
   c) Peru

3) The Anasazi cliff dwellings
   a) USA
   b) Mexico
   c) China

4) The rock city of Petra
   a) Syria
   b) Iran
   c) Jordan

5) The Carnac megaliths
   a) France
   b) Wales
   c) Spain

6) The Sears Tower
a) Canada
b) Hong Kong
c) USA

7) The cave paintings of Altamira
a) Portugal
b) Spain
c) France

8) The Aswan Dam
a) Sudan
b) Egypt
c) Kenya

GENIUS

9) The Royal Palaces of Abomey
a) Benin
b) Zimbabwe
c) South Africa

10) The monasteries of Meteora
a) Turkey
b) Syria
c) Greece

Answers: 1b, 2c, 3a, 4c, 5a, 6c, 7b, 8b, 9a, 10c

MOUNTAINS AND VOLCANOES

EXPERT

1) Where is the volcano Mauna Loa?
   a) Sicily
   b) Hawaii
   c) Fiji

2) What is the longest mountain range in the world?
   a) The Andes
   b) The Himalayas
   c) The Rockies

3) Which mountains are situated in a national park of the same name in New York state?
   a) The Blue Ridge Mountains
   b) The Appalachians
   c) The Adirondacks

4) Where is the volcano Katmai?
   a) The Urals
   b) Alaska
   c) Iceland

5) The second highest mountain in the world, K2 or Godwin Austen, is on the borders of which two countries?
   a) Nepal and China
   b) Bhutan and Nepal
   c) Pakistan and China

6) Where is the active volcano named Mount Erebus?
   a) Antarctica
   b) Greenland
   c) The Urals

7) In which part of the British Isles would you find the Cambrian mountains?
   a) Northern Ireland
   b) Wales
   c) Scotland

EXPERT

8) What is the name of the mountain chain which separates France from Spain?
   a) The Dolomites
   b) The Alps
   c) The Pyrenees

9) Which volcano was responsible for the greatest volcanic explosion ever recorded?
   a) Krakatoa
   b) Stromboli
   c) Tambora

10) What is the highest mountain in Australia?
   a) Mount McKinley
   b) Mount Kosciusko
   c) Mount Cook

Answers: 1b, 2a, 3c, 4b, 5c, 6a, 7b, 8c, 9c, 10b

NORTHERN IRELAND

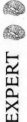

EXPERT

1) Which of these counties was not one of the original six in Northern Ireland?
   a) Armagh
   b) Omagh
   c) Tyrone

2) In which county is the Giant's Causeway?
   a) Antrim
   b) Armagh
   c) Fermanagh

3) What is the highest point in Northern Ireland?
   a) Slieve Donard in the Mountains of Mourne
   b) Mossey's Hill above Gortin, County Tyrone
   c) Trostan in County Antrim

4) What is the county town of Tyrone?
   a) Springfield
   b) Enniskillen
   c) Irvinestown

5) On what river does Belfast lie?
   a) Liffey
   b) Shannon
   c) Lagan

6) In which county of Northern Ireland is the Belleek porcelain factory?
   a) Armagh
   b) Fermanagh
   c) Tyrone

7) The name of which county comes from the Irish word for an oak grove?
   a) Tyrone
   b) Derry
   c) Armagh

8) Where in Northern Ireland would you find the grave of St. Patrick?
   a) Downpatrick
   b) Lurgan
   c) Omagh

9) What is the ancient stronghold of the kings of Ulster, the remains of which lie just west of the city of Armagh?
   a) Tara
   b) New Grange
   c) Navan Fort

10) For what is the Belfast firm of Harland and Wolff best known?
   a) Brewing
   b) Ship-building
   c) Electronics

EXPERT

Answers: 1c, 2a, 3a, 4b, 5c, 6b, 7b, 8a, 9c, 10b

PLACES 1

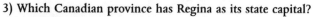

1) On which river does the Italian city of Florence stand?
   a) Arno
   b) Po
   c) Tiber

2) In which English county is the town of Buxton?
   a) Derbyshire
   b) Yorkshire
   c) Staffordshire

3) Which Canadian province has Regina as its state capital?
   a) Manitoba
   b) Nova Scotia
   c) Saskatchewan

4) In which island group is Mindanao?
   a) The Philippines
   b) Indonesia
   c) Micronesia

5) In which country is the volcano Popocatepetl?
   a) Mexico
   b) Peru
   c) Bolivia

EXPERT

6) The Dogger Bank is a hazard to shipping in which body of water?
   a) The English Channel
   b) The North Sea
   c) The Irish Sea

7) In which city are the Tivoli Gardens?
   a) Paris
   b) Rome
   c) Copenhagen

8) On which continent would you find the Mackenzie Mountains?
   a) North America
   b) Australia
   c) Africa

9) Which is the longest river in Asia?
   a) The Mekong River
   b) The Yellow River
   c) The Yangtze River

10) St. Peter Port is the capital of which of the Channel Islands?
   a) Jersey
   b) Guernsey
   c) Alderney

EXPERT

Answers: 1a, 2a, 3c, 4a, 5a, 6b, 7c, 8a, 9c, 10c

PLACES 2

1) What is the state capital of Nebraska?
   a) Bismarck
   b) Lansing
   c) Lincoln

GENIUS

2) If you landed at Tegel airport, in which country would you be?
   a) Austria
   b) Germany
   c) Denmark

3) In which island group is Formentera?
   a) The Canary Islands
   b) The Balearic Islands
   c) The Windward Islands

4) In which ocean is the island of Sao Tome?
   a) Atlantic
   b) Indian
   c) Pacific

5) Where is the Sherman glacier?
   a) Iceland
   b) Alaska
   c) Antarctica

6) Which is the deepest lake in the world?
   a) Lake Titicaca
   b) Lake Baikal
   c) Lake Tanganyika

7) Which two cities are connected by the Suez Canal?
   a) Port Said and Suez
   b) Port Said and Cairo
   c) Suez and Cairo

8) On which island would you find Lake Taupo?
   a) Tasmania
   b) North Island, New Zealand
   c) Madagascar

GENIUS

9) Which of the following countries lies on the equator?
   a) Gabon
   b) Rwanda
   c) Mali

10) Which of the following Australian deserts is the farthest north?
   a) Gibson Desert
   b) Great Victoria Desert
   c) Great Sandy Desert

Answers: 1c, 2b, 3b, 4a, 5b, 6b, 7a, 8b, 9a, 10c

PLACES 3

EXPERT

1) **Where is Cape Wrath?**
   a) Scotland
   b) Canada
   c) South America

2) **To which country does the island of Phuket belong?**
   a) Myanmar
   b) Thailand
   c) Malaysia

3) **Which is the largest in area of these Great Lakes?**
   a) Lake Superior
   b) Lake Michigan
   c) Lake Huron

4) **In which US state is Milwaukee?**
   a) Illinois
   b) Michigan
   c) Wisconsin

5) **Which is the largest state in Australia?**
   a) Western Australia
   b) Queensland
   c) South Australia

6) Which two countries are separated by the Strait of Otranto?
   a) Italy and Albania
   b) Greece and Albania
   c) Italy and Greece

7) Where are the headquarters of UNESCO?
   a) Strasbourg
   b) Brussels
   c) Paris

8) In which country is the city of Split?
   a) Croatia
   b) Hungary
   c) Slovenia

9) Which two countries are connected by the Khyber Pass?
   a) Afghanistan and India
   b) Afghanistan and Pakistan
   c) India and Pakistan

10) Which country administers the Galapagos Islands?
   a) Ecuador
   b) Chile
   c) Venezuela

Answers: 1a, 2b, 3a, 4c, 5a, 6a, 7c, 8a, 9b, 10a

SCOTLAND

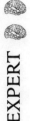

EXPERT

1) **Which Scottish mountain overlooks Fort William?**
   a) Beinn Sgritheall
   b) Ben Macdui
   c) Ben Nevis

2) **What is the Scottish term for a sea estuary?**
   a) An inch
   b) A strath
   c) A firth

3) **Which Scottish castle stands at the confluence of the three lochs: Loch Long, Loch Duich and Loch Alsh?**
   a) Eilean Donan
   b) Castle Urquhart
   c) Kilchurn Castle

4) **Which is the most northerly mainland county of Scotland?**
   a) Ross and Cromarty
   b) Caithness
   c) Nairnshire

5) **Which three Scottish mainland counties border England?**
   a) Berwickshire, Roxburghshire and Dumfriesshire
   b) Berwickshire, Selkirkshire and Kirkcudbrightshire
   c) Roxburghshire, Wigtownshire and Dumfriesshire

6) Which seabird sanctuary is situated in the Firth of Forth, 3 miles east of North Berwick?
   a) St. Kilda
   b) The Bass Rock
   c) Tantallon Castle

7) Which was Scotland's smallest mainland county prior to reorganisation in 1975?
   a) Kinrosshire
   b) Dumbartonshire
   c) Clackmannanshire

8) In which Scottish county is Gretna Green?
   a) Dumfriesshire
   b) Roxburghshire
   c) Ayrshire

9) In which Scottish city can you find the Marischal College and St. Machar's Cathedral?
   a) Dundee
   b) Aberdeen
   c) Glasgow

10) Where, in Edinburgh, is there an unfinished replica of the Parthenon?
    a) On Arthur's Seat
    b) On Calton Hill
    c) In the National Museum of Scotland

Answers: 1c, 2c, 3a, 4b, 5a, 6b, 7c, 8a, 9b, 10b

SEAS AND OCEANS

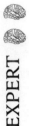

EXPERT

1) **What is unusual about the Caspian Sea?**
   a) It is really a salt-water lake
   b) It contains no salt
   c) It has no tributary rivers

2) **Which body of water was known to the Ancient Greeks as the Propontis?**
   a) The Aegean Sea
   b) The Adriatic Sea
   c) The Sea of Marmara

3) **Which body of water includes Baffin Bay and the Barents Sea?**
   a) The North Atlantic Ocean
   b) The Arctic Ocean
   c) The North Sea

4) **Which sea has its deepest point in the Cayman Trench?**
   a) The Caribbean Sea
   b) The South China Sea
   c) The Mediterranean Sea

5) **In which body of water is Iceland?**
   a) Arctic Ocean
   b) Atlantic Ocean
   c) Baltic Sea

6) In which sea is Australia's Great Barrier Reef?

a) The Coral Sea

b) The Tasman Sea

c) The Gulf of Carpentaria

7) Which ocean contains the deepest trench in the world?

a) Atlantic

b) Arctic

c) Pacific

8) Of which sea is the Bothnian Bay a part?

a) Caspian Sea

b) Baltic Sea

c) Mediterranean Sea

9) Where can the Sargasso Sea be found?

a) North Atlantic Ocean

b) Indian Ocean

c) Arctic Ocean

10) What makes the Red Sea red?

a) The red clay that forms its bed

b) Dead algae

c) Reflection of light on its surface

EXPERT

Answers: 1a, 2c, 3b, 4a, 5b, 6a, 7c, 8b, 9a, 10b

UK ISLANDS

1) What is the capital of the Isle of Man?
   a) Douglas
   b) Ramsay
   c) Peel

2) Which island is the largest of the Inner Hebrides?
   a) Taransay
   b) Skye
   c) Mull

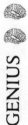

GENIUS

3) Which Holy Island is joined to the mainland by a 3-mile causeway at low tide?
   a) The Holy Island of Lindisfarne
   b) Holy Island, Anglesey
   c) Holy Island, Lamlash Bay, Arran

4) In which group of islands would you find Yell and Nesting?
   a) The Faroe Islands
   b) The Shetland Islands
   c) The Orkney Islands

5) Which is the most southerly of the main islands of the Outer Hebrides?
   a) Harris
   b) South Uist
   c) Barra

6) Which of the Scilly Islands is famous for its beautiful sub-tropical gardens?
   a) St. Mary's
   b) St. Martin's
   c) Tresco

7) In which group of islands would you find the town of Stromness?
   a) The Shetlands
   b) The Outer Hebrides
   c) The Orkney Islands

8) What is the name of the Manx parliament?
   a) The Tynwald
   b) The Althingi
   c) The Stortinget

9) Where is the Isle of May?
   a) In the Firth of Forth
   b) Off the Cornish Coast
   c) In St. George's Channel

10) On which island can you find Fingal's Cave?
   a) Mull
   b) Staffa
   c) Skye

GENIUS

Answers: 1a, 2b, 3a, 4b, 5c, 6c, 7c, 8a, 9a, 10b

WALES

EXPERT

1) Which Welsh river reaches the Irish Sea at the seaside resort of Rhyl?
   a) Conway
   b) Clwyd
   c) Tawe

2) What is the Welsh name for the highest mountain in Wales?
   a) Snowdon
   b) Cader Idris
   c) Yr Wyddfa

3) What is the English name for the city that Welsh-speakers call Abertawe?
   a) Swansea
   b) St. Davids
   c) Cardiff

4) Which Welsh town became a city in 2002?
   a) Newport
   b) Wrexham
   c) St. Davids

5) What is the county town of Dyfed?
   a) Caernafon
   b) Cwmbran
   c) Carmarthen

6) What does Llan mean in Welsh place names like Llanberis, Llangollen and Llanelli?
   a) An enclosed area where a church is often built
   b) An area adjacent to a lake or river
   c) A valley with a river or stream running through it

7) Which is the largest lake in Wales?
   a) Cwellyn
   b) Bala
   c) Glaslyn

8) Where is the National Library of Wales?
   a) Cardiff
   b) Swansea
   c) Aberystwyth

9) What is the Welsh name for Anglesey?
   a) Mona
   b) Ynys Mon
   c) Ynys Enliss

10) When were the first elections of the National Assembly for Wales held?
   a) 1997
   b) 1998
   c) 1999

EXPERT

Answers: 1b, 2c, 3a, 4a, 5c, 6a, 7b, 8c, 9b, 10c

HISTORY
AND
HERITAGE

AMERICAN HISTORY

1) Which German immigrant to the US founded the American Fur Company in 1808 and became one of the country's richest men?
   a) John Jacob Astor
   b) Cornelius Vanderbilt
   c) John D. Rockefeller

2) Which British general surrendered at Yorktown in October 1781, effectively ending the American War of Independence?
   a) Howe
   b) Wolfe
   c) Cornwallis

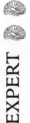

EXPERT

3) What was held at Seneca Falls, New York in 1848?
   a) The first women's rights convention
   b) The inaugural meeting of the Republican Party
   c) The first anti-slavery convention

4) Which American city was known as Yerba Buena until 1847?
   a) Los Angeles
   b) San Francisco
   c) Las Vegas

5) In what year did the Spanish-American War begin?
   a) 1888
   b) 1898
   c) 1908

6) In American history, for what is Betsy Ross remembered?
   a) Being elected as the first woman senator
   b) Being the first ex-slave to vote in a presidential election
   c) Making the first US flag

7) Who was American President at the time of the Wall Street Crash in 1929?
   a) Calvin Coolidge
   b) Woodrow Wilson
   c) Herbert Hoover

EXPERT

8) In which state was a biology teacher, John Scopes, tried in 1925 for teaching Darwin's theory of evolution to his pupils?
   a) Tennessee
   b) Alabama
   c) Georgia

9) Which Native American tribe was forced into exile in 1838–9 on what became known as 'The Trail of Tears'?
   a) Sioux
   b) Seminole
   c) Cherokee

10) Who was the first person to sign the Declaration of Independence in 1776?
   a) John Hancock
   b) Benjamin Franklin
   c) George Washington

Answers: 1a, 2c, 3a, 4b, 5b, 6c, 7c, 8a, 9c, 10a

ANCIENT GREECE AND ROME

1) In Ancient Greece, what was a hoplite?
   a) A foot soldier
   b) A household slave
   c) A householder

2) Who was the king of Troy at the beginning of the Trojan War?
   a) Agamemnon
   b) Priam
   c) Hector

GENIUS

3) Which Roman general and statesman led the aristocratic party in the civil war of 88–86 BC and eventually became dictator of Rome?
   a) Julius Caesar
   b) Sulla
   c) Pompey

4) What was the name of the sister of Alexander the Great?
   a) Olympias
   b) Roxane
   c) Cleopatra

5) Which city did Rome destroy in the Punic Wars?
   a) Constantinople
   b) Carthage
   c) Athens

6) Which of the following Roman Emperors originally came from Africa?
   a) Septimus Severus
   b) Constantine
   c) Marcus Aurelius

7) Whose second wife was called Poppaea?
   a) Alexander the Great
   b) Augustus
   c) Nero

8) What was the name of the harbour city of ancient Rome?
   a) Ostia
   b) Testaccio
   c) Trastevere

9) To which of the Olympian gods was the Parthenon dedicated?
   a) Athena
   b) Zeus
   c) Hera

10) What was unusual about the consul Incitatus, elected between 37 and 41 AD?
   a) She was the first woman elected to public office
   b) He was the first plebeian consul
   c) He was a horse

Answers: 1a, 2b, 3b, 4c, 5b, 6a, 7c, 8a, 9a, 10c

THE ANCIENT WORLD

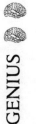

GENIUS

1) Which Emperor of Persia was defeated by Alexander the Great?
   a) Darius III
   b) Cyrus II
   c) Cambyses II

2) In which ancient empire was the city of Nineveh?
   a) Assyrian
   b) Egyptian
   c) Persian

3) In which country would you find the ancient Mayan city of Tikal?
   a) Guatemala
   b) Mexico
   c) Belize

4) Who was the first man to decipher Egyptian hieroglyphics?
   a) Howard Carter
   b) Michael Ventris
   c) Jean-Francois Champollion

5) On which island can you find the megalithic site of Callanish?
   a) The Isle of Lewis
   b) The Isle of Skye
   c) The Isle of Arran

6) Which of the following is the closest translation of the word Pharaoh?
   a) Great leader
   b) Great priest
   c) Great house

7) From which century do the Qin Shi Huang terracotta warriors and horses of China date?
   a) 1st century AD
   b) 3rd century AD
   c) 3rd century BC

8) In which ancient culture did the myths of Gilgamesh originate?
   a) Egyptian
   b) Sumerian
   c) Persian

9) Who was the Assyrian and Babylonian goddess of fertility and childbirth?
   a) Mylitta
   b) Dagon
   c) Baal

10) To what did the Egyptian pharaoh Amenhotep IV change his name?
   a) Rameses
   b) Tutankhamun
   c) Akhenaten

Answers: 1a, 2a, 3a, 4c, 5a, 6c, 7c, 8b, 9a, 10c

GENIUS

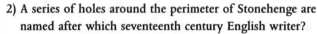

ARCHAEOLOGY

1) Who sold the Elgin Marbles, now in the British Museum, to Lord Elgin in the early nineteenth century?
   a) The Greeks
   b) The Turks
   c) The British Government

2) A series of holes around the perimeter of Stonehenge are named after which seventeenth century English writer?
   a) Andrew Marvell
   b) Thomas Middleton
   c) John Aubrey

3) Which ancient Egyptian is credited with the building of the Step Pyramid at Saqqara?
   a) Rameses II
   b) Imhotep
   c) Hatshepsut

4) Heinrich Schliemann sent a telegram to the King of Greece, saying, 'I have looked upon the face of Agamemnon'. Which ancient site was he excavating at the time?
   a) Mycenae
   b) Troy
   c) Knossos

5) When the ancient Egyptians mummified the bodies of their pharaohs, how did they remove the brains?
   a) Through the nose
   b) Through the mouth
   c) Through the ears

GENIUS

6) What were discovered in caves at Altamira in Spain in 1879?
   a) Prehistoric paintings
   b) Neanderthal skeletons
   c) Preserved mammoths

7) Giovanni Belzoni was one of the earliest European excavators of Egyptian antiquities. What profession did he follow before he became an archaeologist?
   a) Teacher
   b) Lawyer
   c) Circus strongman

8) Which archaeologist was the first to develop and apply a method of statistical analysis to material from Egyptian burial sites?
   a) Heinrich Schliemann
   b) Howard Carter
   c) William Flinders Petrie

9) Where can the Neolithic settlement of Skara Brae be found?
   a) Norway
   b) The Shetland Islands
   c) The Orkney Islands

10) Which ancient American city was discovered by Hiram Bingham in 1911?
   a) Tenochtitlan
   b) Machu Picchu
   c) Cuzco

GENIUS

Answers: 1b, 2c, 3b, 4a, 5a, 6a, 7c, 8c, 9c, 10b

THE BIBLE

EXPERT

1) In the Old Testament who was David's closest friend and the son of King Saul?
   a) Goliath
   b) Jonathan
   c) Absalom

2) Which Old Testament prophet gives his name to someone who habitually foretells doom and disaster?
   a) Jeremiah
   b) Jonah
   c) Job

3) According to John's Gospel, what was Jesus's first miracle?
   a) Feeding the five thousand
   b) Walking on the waters of Lake Galilee
   c) Turning water into wine at the wedding in Cana

4) In the Book of Judges, how did Jael kill the fleeing Canaanite general Sisera?
   a) By driving a tent peg through his head
   b) By pouring poison in his wine
   c) By setting wild dogs on him

5) What was the name of the child God gave to Eve in place of the murdered Abel?
   a) Micah
   b) Jacob
   c) Seth

6) Golgotha was the site of Jesus's crucifixion. What does the word 'Golgotha' mean?
   a) The Potter's Field
   b) The Place of the Skull
   c) The Garden of Earthly Delights

7) In the New Testament, who was the brother of Mary and Martha?
   a) Lazarus
   b) Simon Peter
   c) Joseph of Arimathea

8) What was the name of John the Baptist's mother?
   a) Ruth
   b) Naomi
   c) Elizabeth

9) In Genesis, for what is Nimrod most famed?
   a) He is a great hunter
   b) He is an expert chariot driver
   c) He has a beautiful singing voice

10) Which of the following is not one of the sons of Noah?
    a) Ham
    b) Abednego
    c) Japheth

EXPERT

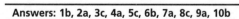

Answers: 1b, 2a, 3c, 4a, 5c, 6b, 7a, 8c, 9a, 10b

BRITISH HISTORY 1

NOVICE

1) Who was responsible for the founding and organisation of the Model Parliament in 1265?
   a) Edward I
   b) Simon de Montfort
   c) William the Marshall

2) In which British city did the Peterloo Massacre of 1819 take place?
   a) Birmingham
   b) Liverpool
   c) Manchester

3) What disaster occurred in London in 1665?
   a) The Great Fire of London
   b) The burning of the Savoy Palace
   c) The start of the Great Plague

4) What tax was levied by British governments between 1696 and 1851?
   a) Income Tax
   b) Salt Tax
   c) Window Tax

5) Which parliamentary act in 1534 severed links between the Church of England and the Church of Rome?
   a) The Act of Supremacy
   b) The Dissolution of the Monasteries
   c) The Act of Settlement

6) In which year was Magna Carta signed at Runnymede by
King John?
a) 1399
b) 1257
c) 1215

7) In which county are the remains of the Roman settlement
of Vindolanda?
a) Northumberland
b) Cumbria
c) Yorkshire

NOVICE

8) With which reforming act of parliament was Richard
Cobden associated?
a) The Repeal of the Corn Laws
b) The Abolition of Slavery
c) The Reform Act of 1832

9) What name was given to the followers of John Wycliffe?
a) The Lollards
b) The Chartists
c) The Luddites

10) Who succeeded Asquith as British Prime Minister in
1916?
a) Stanley Baldwin
b) David Lloyd George
c) Henry Campbell-Bannerman

Answers: 1b, 2c, 3c, 4c, 5a, 6c, 7a, 8a, 9a, 10b

BRITISH HISTORY 2

EXPERT

1) In which county did the Tolpuddle Martyrs form their illegal trade union in 1834?
   a) Somerset
   b) Wiltshire
   c) Dorset

2) Who was the first Prime Minister to occupy Chequers?
   a) David Lloyd George
   b) Winston Churchill
   c) William Pitt the Younger

3) On which saint's day in 1415 did the Battle of Agincourt take place?
   a) St. David's
   b) St. George's
   c) St. Crispin's

4) What was William Lamb's title when he was British Prime Minister?
   a) Lord Salisbury
   b) Lord Melbourne
   c) Lord Liverpool

5) How were the ports of Dover, Hastings, Hythe, Romney and Sandwich once collectively known?
   a) The Channel Ports
   b) The Cinque Ports
   c) The Kent Ports

6) Which English hero was born at Burnham Thorpe in Norfolk?
   a) Henry V
   b) The Black Prince
   c) Nelson

7) Which city was the capital of England before London?
   a) Winchester
   b) Cirencester
   c) York

8) Who was killed at Kirk o' Fields in Edinburgh in 1567?
   a) Mary, Queen of Scots
   b) Lord Darnley
   c) David Rizzio

9) The mother of which famous politician was an American heiress called Jenny Jerome?
   a) Stanley Baldwin
   b) Clement Attlee
   c) Winston Churchill

10) What is the name usually given to the ship that sank in the English Channel in 1120, drowning the heir to the throne and many others?
   a) *The White Ship*
   b) *The Black Ship*
   c) *The Red Ship*

EXPERT

Answers: 1c, 2a, 3c, 4b, 5b, 6c, 7a, 8b, 9c, 10a

BRITISH HISTORY 3

1) How old was Queen Victoria when she died?
   a) 79
   b) 81
   c) 83

2) Who was the first Labour Chancellor of the Exchequer?
   a) Hugh Dalton
   b) Ramsay MacDonald
   c) Philip Snowden

GENIUS

3) How many names were there in the first British telephone directory, issued in 1880?
   a) 55
   b) 255
   c) 1,555

4) What did George Shillibeer introduce to London in 1829?
   a) Traffic lights
   b) Horse-drawn bus service
   c) Newspaper kiosks

5) In which government office were trade unions banned in 1984?
   a) MI5
   b) Government Communications HQ
   c) The Department of Trade and Industry

6) In which ancient forest are licensed shepherds known as 'Sheep Badgers'?
a) The New Forest
b) Sherwood Forest
c) The Forest of Dean

7) Which post did William Gilbert hold at the courts of both Elizabeth I and James I?
a) Jester
b) Royal Physician
c) Lord Chancellor

8) In what year did England lose Calais, its last possession in France?
a) 1458
b) 1558
c) 1658

9) The grave of which legendary Briton supposedly lies under Platform 8 at King's Cross station?
a) Robin Hood
b) King Arthur
c) Boudicca

10) Who was the mother of Lady Jane Grey, Queen of England for nine days in 1553?
a) Frances Brandon, Marchioness of Dorset, niece to Henry VIII
b) Mary, Duchess of Suffolk, sister to Henry VIII
c) Margaret, Queen of Scotland, elder daughter of Henry VII

Answers: 1b, 2c, 3b, 4b, 5b, 6c, 7b, 8b, 9c, 10a

BRITISH PRINCES AND PRINCESSES

1) What was the name of the eldest son of William the Conqueror who never wore the crown of England?
a) William
b) Geoffrey
c) Robert

2) What was the name of George IV's only legitimate daughter who died in childbirth in 1817 at the age of 21?
a) Charlotte
b) Caroline
c) Elizabeth

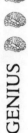

3) William, the prince who drowned during a storm in the Channel in 1120, was the son of which king?
a) Henry I
b) Henry II
c) Henry III

4) Whose book *The Little Princesses* caused its author to be ostracised by the Royal Family?
a) Andrew Morton
b) Marion Crawford
c) Sarah, Duchess of York

5) Prince Arthur, grandson of Henry II, was thought to have the most legitimate claim to the throne. Which uncle ensured his own succession instead?
a) John
b) Richard
c) Henry IV

6) What was the name of the only daughter of Queen Mary and George V, who was given the title of The Princess Royal?
   a) Louise Victoria Alexandra Dagmar, known as Princess Louise
   b) Victoria Elizabeth Mary Alice, known as Princess Alice
   c) Victoria Alexandra Alice Mary, known as Princess Mary

7) Who was the son of Henry VII who married Catherine of Aragon and died in 1502?
   a) Arthur
   b) Edward
   c) Henry

8) Which Stuart king had an elder brother called Henry Frederick who died in 1612?
   a) James II
   b) Charles I
   c) Charles II

9) Which Princess was 5th in line to the British throne at the beginning of 2004?
   a) Princess Anne, The Princess Royal
   b) Princess Eugenie of York
   c) Princess Beatrice of York

10) What was the title taken by Albert Victor, the eldest son of Edward VII, who died in 1892?
   a) Duke of Cornwall
   b) Duke of Clarence
   c) Prince of Wales

GENIUS

Answers: 1c, 2a, 3a, 4b, 5a, 6c, 7a, 8b, 9c, 10b

CASTLES AND STATELY HOMES

EXPERT

1) Which historic house is the seat of the Earl of Bradford?
   a) Weston Park
   b) Wilton House
   c) Ragley Hall

2) Which castle houses the regimental museum of the Royal Northumberland Fusiliers?
   a) Bamburgh
   b) Warkworth
   c) Alnwick

3) Which 13th century castle can be found on the island of Anglesey?
   a) Conwy
   b) Beaumaris
   c) Chepstow

4) Which historic building was the home of Anne Boleyn's family during her courtship by Henry VIII?
   a) Sudbury Hall
   b) Hever Castle
   c) Rochester Castle

5) Which castle houses Queen Mary's Dolls' House?
   a) Windsor
   b) Edinburgh
   c) Balmoral

6) Which of the following great houses can be found on the Isle of Wight?
   a) Chatsworth House
   b) Blenheim Palace
   c) Osborne House

7) Who built the castle of Neuschwanstein in Germany?
   a) King Ludwig of Bavaria
   b) Kaiser Wilhelm II
   c) Bismarck

8) In a medieval castle what was the 'garderobe'?
   a) Storage room
   b) Toilet
   c) Lord's private quarters

EXPERT

9) Which English King ordered the building of the Welsh castles of Beaumaris, Harlech and Caernarfon?
   a) Edward I
   b) Edward II
   c) Edward III

10) Which historic house is the seat of the Dukes of Bedford?
   a) Longleat
   b) Eaton Hall
   c) Woburn Abbey

Answers: 1a, 2c, 3b, 4b, 5a, 6c, 7a, 8b, 9a, 10c

CATHEDRALS AND CHURCHES

1) In which English cathedral is the Mappa Mundi kept?
   a) Worcester
   b) Hereford
   c) Gloucester

2) Which English cathedral suffered a major fire in July 1984?
   a) St. Paul's, London
   b) Chichester
   c) York Minster

EXPERT

3) Who ordered the building of St. Basil's Cathedral in Moscow?
   a) Catherine the Great
   b) Ivan the Terrible
   c) Peter the Great

4) In which cathedral were all but six of the Kings of France crowned?
   a) Notre Dame, Paris
   b) Rheims
   c) Chartres

5) The gothic church Santa Maria Gloriosa dei Frari can be found in which Italian city?
   a) Venice
   b) Florence
   c) Rome

6) In a church, what is a reredos?
   a) Type of font
   b) Type of screen behind the altar
   c) Type of wooden cross above the altar

7) From which language does the word 'cathedral' derive?
   a) Hebrew
   b) Latin
   c) Greek

8) Who designed the new Coventry Cathedral, which was consecrated in 1962?
   a) Sir Norman Foster
   b) Sir Edwin Lutyens
   c) Sir Basil Spence

9) Which English king is buried in Canterbury Cathedral?
   a) Henry IV
   b) Henry VII
   c) Henry VIII

10) In a church or cathedral, where would you usually find 'misericords'?
   a) On the roof
   b) Under seats in the choir
   c) Behind the altar

EXPERT

Answers: 1b, 2c, 3b, 4b, 5a, 6b, 7c, 8c, 9a, 10b

DATES

In which year did the following historical events take place?

1) The death of the Duke of Wellington
   a) 1832
   b) 1842
   c) 1852

2) The founding of the Bank of England
   a) 1634
   b) 1664
   c) 1694

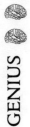

GENIUS

3) The Great Fire of London
   a) 1656
   b) 1666
   c) 1676

4) Yuri Gagarin's first spaceflight
   a) 1957
   b) 1959
   c) 1961

5) The General Strike
   a) 1922
   b) 1926
   c) 1930

6) The first meeting of Stanley and Livingstone
   a) 1871
   b) 1874
   c) 1877

7) The burning of Joan of Arc
   a) 1411
   b) 1421
   c) 1431

8) The crowning of Charlemagne as Holy Roman Emperor
   a) 700
   b) 800
   c) 900

GENIUS

9) The birth of Shakespeare
   a) 1556
   b) 1560
   c) 1564

10) The Gunfight at the OK Corral
    a) 1881
    b) 1886
    c) 1891

Answers: 1c, 2c, 3b, 4c, 5b, 6a, 7c, 8b, 9c, 10a

FAMOUS MURDERS

1) The son of which American folk hero was kidnapped and murdered in the 1930s?
   a) Babe Ruth
   b) Charles Lindbergh
   c) Douglas Fairbanks

2) Which notorious murderer lived at 10 Rillington Place?
   a) Dr Crippen
   b) John Christie
   c) Dennis Nilsen

3) Where was President Abraham Lincoln when he was assassinated in 1865?
   a) At the White House
   b) In his barber's chair
   c) In a box at Ford's Theatre, Washington

4) How is the serial killer Peter Sutcliffe better known?
   a) The Boston Strangler
   b) The Black Dahlia Killer
   c) The Yorkshire Ripper

5) In 1922 William Desmond Taylor was shot dead in his fashionable California home. What was his occupation?
   a) He was a Hollywood film director
   b) He was a newspaper tycoon
   c) He was a best-selling novelist

6) Who killed John Lennon outside his apartment block in New York in 1980?
   a) John Hinckley
   b) Mark Chapman
   c) James Earl Ray

7) What was remarkable about the Victorian murderer John Lee?
   a) He was the youngest person ever executed in Britain
   b) He was the last civilian to be executed by firing squad
   c) Three attempts to hang him all failed

8) Which rap star was shot dead in September 1996?
   a) Tupac Shakur
   b) Biggie Smalls
   c) Puffy Combs

9) By what name is the 1827 killing of Maria Marten by William Corder better known?
   a) The Red Lodge Murder
   b) The Red Barn Murder
   c) The Red Mansion Murder

10) Who wrote *The Executioner's Song*, a book about the life and death of the American murderer Gary Gilmore?
    a) Truman Capote
    b) Norman Mailer
    c) George Plimpton

NOVICE

Answers: 1b, 2b, 3c, 4c, 5a, 6b, 7c, 8a, 9b, 10b

GREAT BATTLES

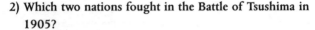

1) Which King was killed at the Battle of Lutzen in 1632?
   a) Louis XIV of France
   b) Gustavus Adolphus of Sweden
   c) Philip II of Spain

2) Which two nations fought in the Battle of Tsushima in 1905?
   a) Russia and Japan
   b) China and Japan
   c) Russia and China

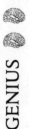

GENIUS

3) In which war did the Battle of Antietam take place?
   a) The Second World War
   b) The American Civil War
   c) The Boer War

4) Which Scottish leader was defeated at the Battle of Falkirk in 1298?
   a) Robert the Bruce
   b) John Balliol
   c) William Wallace

5) Which of these famous generals was present at the Battle of Ramillies?
   a) Duke of Marlborough
   b) Duke of Wellington
   c) Duke of Cumberland

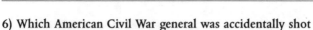

6) Which American Civil War general was accidentally shot and killed by his own men?
   a) Robert E. Lee
   b) Thomas 'Stonewall' Jackson
   c) Ambrose Burnside

7) At which battle in 1066 did King Harold defeat an invading force from Norway?
   a) Battle of Towton
   b) Battle of Maldon
   c) Battle of Stamford Bridge

8) Which of the following battles was *not* a victory for Alexander the Great?
   a) Battle of Issus
   b) Battle of Gaugamela
   c) Battle of Zama

GENIUS

9) Which English king, at the Battle of Dettingen, was the last to lead his troops personally into battle?
   a) George I
   b) George II
   c) George III

10) In what year was the Battle of Austerlitz?
   a) 1799
   b) 1805
   c) 1813

Answers: 1b, 2a, 3b, 4c, 5a, 6b, 7c, 8c, 9b, 10b

MONARCHS

1) Which European country was ruled by monarchs of the House of Braganza?
   a) Spain
   b) Portugal
   c) Greece

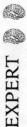

2) Which English monarch had a lover called Piers Gaveston?
   a) Richard I
   b) Elizabeth I
   c) Edward II

3) Which English king was the illegitimate son of Robert the Devil?
   a) Stephen
   b) William I
   c) John

4) Which of these monarchs reigned for the most number of years?
   a) King Louis XIV of France
   b) Queen Victoria of Great Britain
   c) Emperor Franz-Josef of Austria

5) Which Egyptian pharaoh was married to Nefertiti?
   a) Akhenaten
   b) Tutankhamun
   c) Rameses II

6) To which Catholic throne did Henry III, Protestant king of Navarre, succeed in 1589?
a) Portugal
b) Spain
c) France

7) What was the name of the Inca emperor imprisoned and executed in 1533 by the Spanish conquistadors led by Pizarro?
a) Montezuma
b) Atahualpa
c) Tupac Amaru

8) What is the name of the current Royal House of Sweden?
a) Vasa
b) Bernadotte
c) Gustavson

9) Who was the last king of Greece, finally deposed in 1973?
a) Andreas II
b) Konstantinos II
c) Nikos III

10) What is the name of the present Japanese emperor?
a) Hirohito
b) Yoshihito
c) Akihito

EXPERT

Answers: 1b, 2c, 3b, 4a, 5a, 6c, 7b, 8b, 9b, 10c

MUSEUMS AND GALLERIES

1) In which British city can you find the Whitworth Art Gallery?
   a) Glasgow
   b) Manchester
   c) Liverpool

EXPERT

2) In which museum can the Rosetta Stone be seen?
   a) The Louvre
   b) The British Museum
   c) The Cairo Museum of Antiquities

3) Which art gallery was founded by a 19th century sugar magnate?
   a) The Wallace Collection
   b) The Guggenheim Museum of Modern Art
   c) The Tate Gallery

4) Which artist once said, 'Give me a museum and I will fill it'?
   a) Pablo Picasso
   b) Salvador Dali
   c) L. S. Lowry

5) Which of the following statements is true of James Smithson, the man whose bequest led to the foundation of the Smithsonian Institution in the USA?
   a) He was illiterate
   b) He never visited the USA
   c) He was revealed as a swindler after his death

6) In which London art gallery can Frans Hals's painting *The Laughing Cavalier* be seen?
   a) The National Gallery
   b) The Dulwich Picture Gallery
   c) The Wallace Collection

7) Which London Museum was designed by Alfred Waterhouse?
   a) The Natural History Museum
   b) The Victoria and Albert Museum
   c) The British Museum

EXPERT

8) The Prado is the national museum of Spain. What does Prado mean in Spanish?
   a) Palace
   b) Meadow
   c) Bridge

9) Who designed the Guggenheim Museum in Bilbao?
   a) Frank Gehry
   b) I. M. Pei
   c) Richard Rodgers

10) In which city is the Hermitage Museum?
   a) Moscow
   b) Dresden
   c) St. Petersburg

Answers: 1b, 2b, 3c, 4a, 5b, 6c, 7a, 8b, 9a, 10c

WOMEN IN HISTORY

1) In 1907 who was the first woman to receive the Order of Merit?
   a) Elizabeth Garrett Anderson
   b) Florence Nightingale
   c) Marie Curie

2) Which woman mathematician, astronomer, and Platonic philosopher was murdered in Alexandria in 415 AD?
   a) Thais
   b) Heloise
   c) Hypatia

EXPERT

3) Who was the first English woman to earn her living by writing plays and novels?
   a) Catherine Trotter
   b) Aphra Behn
   c) Mary Pix

4) For what is Mary Seacole remembered?
   a) She was a pioneering nurse and heroine of the Crimean War
   b) She was the first woman to graduate from Cambridge University
   c) She became a pirate and lived in disguise as a man for many years

5) The Trung sisters, Trung Trac and Trung Nhi, are venerated in Vietnam for their heroic resistance to which nation in AD 40?
   a) Japan
   b) Cambodia
   c) China

6) Who was the first woman in space?
   a) Sally Ride
   b) Irina Rodnina
   c) Valentina Tereshkova

7) Who was the first woman to run for American president?
   a) Victoria Claflin Woodhull
   b) Harriet Beecher Stowe
   c) Eleanor Roosevelt

8) Which of these pioneer women aviators disappeared while trying to fly around the world?
   a) Amy Johnson
   b) Amelia Earhart
   c) Beryl Markham

9) In which of the arts did Angelica Kauffmann achieve fame in 18th century England?
   a) Painting
   b) Theatre
   c) Music

10) In which city did Emmeline Pankhurst found the Women's Social and Political Union in 1903?
   a) London
   b) Liverpool
   c) Manchester

EXPERT

Answers: 1b, 2c, 3b, 4a, 5c, 6c, 7a, 8b, 9a, 10c

WORLD HISTORY 1

1) Of which country was Antonio de Salazar dictator from 1932 to 1968?
   a) Chile
   b) Brazil
   c) Portugal

2) Which of the following countries never had a colony on the North American mainland?
   a) Germany
   b) The Netherlands
   c) Sweden

NOVICE

3) What was the codename given to Hitler's planned invasion of Britain in 1940?
   a) Operation Barbarossa
   b) Operation Sea Lion
   c) Operation Dolphin

4) Of which nation was King Mongkut the ruler from 1851 to 1868?
   a) Thailand
   b) Burma (Myanmar)
   c) Vietnam

5) In French history, for what is Claude-Joseph Rouget de Lisle remembered?
   a) Designing the Sacre Coeur cathedral in Paris
   b) Being the first man killed in the 1848 Revolution
   c) Composing the *Marseillaise*

6) Which leader of the Zulus changed the tribe from a small clan into a nation that held sway over a large proportion of Southern Africa in the 19th century?
   a) Shaka
   b) Cetshwayo
   c) Dingane

7) Which two navies fought each other in the Battle of Salamis in 480 BC?
   a) The Spartan and the Athenian
   b) The Greek and the Persian
   c) The Roman and the Greek

8) Who founded the International Red Cross?
   a) Henri Dunant
   b) Albert Schweizer
   c) Alfred Nobel

9) In which century was the Holy Roman Empire finally dissolved?
   a) The 19th
   b) The 18th
   c) The 17th

10) In the 1890s which of the following African countries defeated an invading Italian army?
   a) Uganda
   b) Angola
   c) Ethiopia

Answers: 1c, 2a, 3b, 4a, 5c, 6a, 7b, 8a, 9a, 10c

NOVICE

WORLD HISTORY 2

EXPERT

1) In addition to Catherine Parr, which of Henry VIII's wives survived him?
   a) Catherine Howard
   b) Katherine of Aragon
   c) Anne of Cleves

2) Where was the first permanent English settlement in North America, founded in 1607?
   a) Cupar's Cove, Newfoundland
   b) Jamestown, Virginia
   c) Plymouth, Massachusetts

3) The "Anschluss" refers to the union of Nazi Germany with which other European country?
   a) Austria
   b) Poland
   c) Czechoslovakia

4) Which of these South American countries was named in honour of the man who drew up its first constitution?
   a) Ecuador
   b) Venezuela
   c) Bolivia

5) What nationality was the seafarer and explorer Vasco da Gama?
   a) Spanish
   b) Portuguese
   c) Italian

6) Which King of France issued the Edict of Nantes, giving freedom of conscience to the Protestant Huguenots, in 1598?
   a) Henri III
   b) Henri IV
   c) Louis XIV

7) Which ruler was responsible for the destruction of the temple at Jerusalem in 588 BC?
   a) Nebuchadnezzar
   b) Xerxes
   c) Alexander the Great

8) In which city was Martin Luther King Jr. assassinated in 1968?
   a) Dallas
   b) Chicago
   c) Memphis

9) The early history of which island was written in the *Landnamabok* (Book of Settlements)?
   a) Greenland
   b) Iceland
   c) The Isle of Man

10) Which country was formerly known as Siam?
   a) Myanmar
   b) Iran
   c) Thailand

EXPERT

Answers: 1c, 2b, 3a, 4c, 5b, 6b, 7a, 8c, 9b, 10c

WORLD HISTORY 3

1) Which nation was unified by the warrior Toyotomi
   Hideyoshi in 1590?
   a) Korea
   b) Japan
   c) Indonesia

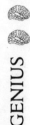

2) In Ancient Rome what was the Cloaca Maxima?
   a) The second largest aqueduct in the Roman Empire
   b) The great drain of Rome
   c) The main road from the Roman to the port of Ostia

3) In the French Revolutionary calendar, introduced in 1793,
   what did the name of the month Brumaire mean?
   a) Month of fog
   b) Month of rain
   c) Month of harvest

4) Which war was brought to an end by the Treaty of
   Vereeniging?
   a) The Seven Years' War
   b) The Boer War
   c) The War of the Spanish Succession

5) In the 1850s why was Edward Hargreaves awarded
   £10,000 by the government of New South Wales?
   a) He captured the outlaw Ned Kelly
   b) He was the first to find gold in the state
   c) He had been wrongfully transported to Australia thirty
      years earlier

GENIUS

6) Who was the first Pope since St. Peter to visit the Holy Land?
   a) Pope John Paul II
   b) Pope John XXIII
   c) Pope Paul VI

7) Who was the first President of Israel?
   a) David Ben-Gurion
   b) Chaim Weizmann
   c) Alexander Herzen

8) In which year did the Republic of Bangladesh declare its independence from Pakistan?
   a) 1947
   b) 1971
   c) 1992

9) Where did Alexander the Great die?
   a) Alexandria
   b) Athens
   c) Babylon

10) Of which state was Sir James ('Rajah') Brooke ruler from 1841 to 1868?
   a) Singapore
   b) Sarawak
   c) Malaya

GENIUS

Answers: 1b, 2b, 3a, 4b, 5b, 6c, 7b, 8b, 9c, 10b

WORLD WAR ONE

1) Which general commanded the British Expeditionary Force when it crossed the Channel to France in August 1914?
   a) General Sir John French
   b) General Sir Douglas Haig
   c) General Sir Herbert Horatio Kitchener

EXPERT

2) How is the Third Battle of Ypres better known?
   a) Battle of Verdun
   b) Battle of the Somme
   c) Battle of Passchendaele

3) At which battle in August 1914 did Hindenburg and Ludendorff defeat the Russians?
   a) Tannenberg
   b) Brest-Litovsk
   c) Jena

4) What was the real name of the German air ace known as the Red Baron?
   a) Von Bülow
   b) Von Falkenhayn
   c) Von Richthofen

5) Who was the admiral commanding the British fleet during the Battle of Jutland?
   a) Byng
   b) Fisher
   c) Jellicoe

6) In which battle of 1917 did the first mass attack by tanks take place?
   a) Mons
   b) Cambrai
   c) Verdun

7) Which passenger ship was sunk by a German U-boat in May 1915?
   a) Mauretania
   b) Titanic
   c) Lusitania

8) In which city was Archduke Franz Ferdinand assassinated in June 1914?
   a) Belgrade
   b) Sarajevo
   c) Vienna

9) Who was the French general who took command at the Battle of Verdun in February 1916?
   a) Pétain
   b) Joffre
   c) Foch

10) To which country did the German Kaiser, Wilhelm II, retire after the war?
    a) Switzerland
    b) Sweden
    c) Holland

EXPERT

Answers: 1a, 2c, 3a, 4c, 5c, 6b, 7c, 8b, 9a, 10c

WORLD WAR TWO

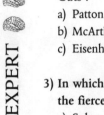

EXPERT

1) Operation Barbarossa was the codename given to the Nazi invasion of which country?
   a) Norway
   b) Soviet Union
   c) Poland

2) Which American general was nicknamed 'Blood and Guts'?
   a) Patton
   b) McArthur
   c) Eisenhower

3) In which group of islands is Guadalcanal, scene of some of the fiercest fighting in the war in the Pacific?
   a) Solomon Islands
   b) The Philippines
   c) Indonesia

4) Which general was commander of British troops in Singapore at the time of the surrender to the Japanese in 1942?
   a) Wavell
   b) Slim
   c) Percival

5) Which of the following was not one of the codenames for the beaches on which Allied troops landed on D-Day?
   a) Juno
   b) Omaha
   c) Silver

6) Who was the Nazi Minister of Armaments from 1942 to 1945?
   a) Von Papen
   b) Speer
   c) Himmler

7) On which day in 1941 did the Japanese bomb Pearl Harbour?
   a) October 7th
   b) November 7th
   c) December 7th

EXPERT

8) Who was America's most decorated soldier of World War II, later to become a Hollywood film star?
   a) Lt. Audie Murphy
   b) Sergeant J. T. York
   c) Captain Harold Russell

9) Which South American country declared war on Germany less than six weeks before the end of hostilities in Europe?
   a) Argentina
   b) Colombia
   c) Brazil

10) Who was the commander of the German army that was surrounded and destroyed at Stalingrad in 1943?
   a) Paulus
   b) Rommel
   c) Guderian

Answers: 1b, 2a, 3a, 4c, 5c, 6b, 7c, 8a, 9a, 10c

LANGUAGE
AND
LITERATURE

AMERICAN LITERATURE

EXPERT

1) Ernest Hemingway wrote that 'all modern American literature comes from one book.' Which book?
   a) *Huckleberry Finn* by Mark Twain
   b) *Moby Dick* by Herman Melville
   c) *The Scarlet Letter* by Nathaniel Hawthorne

2) Who wrote *Breakfast at Tiffany's* and *In Cold Blood*?
   a) Gore Vidal
   b) Truman Capote
   c) Norman Mailer

3) What is the name of the family of prodigies and geniuses that features in many of J. D. Salinger's short stories?
   a) Glass
   b) Holden
   c) Caulfield

4) Which American dramatist wrote *Who's Afraid of Virginia Woolf*?
   a) Arthur Miller
   b) Thornton Wilder
   c) Edward Albee

5) Which 19th century American novelist wrote a novella called *The Man That Corrupted Hadleyburg*?
   a) Mark Twain
   b) Nathaniel Hawthorne
   c) Herman Melville

6) For how many years did Rip Van Winkle sleep in the story by Washington Irving?
   a) 10
   b) 20
   c) 50

7) Whom did the poet Allen Ginsberg once describe as 'the new Buddha of American prose'?
   a) Timothy Leary
   b) Norman Mailer
   c) Jack Kerouac

8) What is the name of the novel by Jeffrey Eugenides that won the Pulitzer Prize for Fiction in 2003?
   a) *The Little Friend*
   b) *The Corrections*
   c) *Middlesex*

9) Who wrote *Tender is the Night?*
   a) Raymond Chandler
   b) John Steinbeck
   c) F. Scott Fitzgerald

10) In which American state was the playwright Tennessee Williams born?
   a) Tennessee
   b) Mississippi
   c) Alabama

EXPERT

Answers: 1a, 2b, 3a, 4c, 5a, 6b, 7c, 8c, 9c, 10b

CRIME FICTION

1) In which Agatha Christie novel did Hercule Poirot make his first appearance?
   a) *Death on the Nile*
   b) *The Murder of Roger Ackroyd*
   c) *The Mysterious Affair at Styles*

2) Which American crime writer worked as a detective for Pinkerton's Agency before ill health forced him to retire and take up writing?
   a) Raymond Chandler
   b) Dashiell Hammett
   c) John D. MacDonald

3) Who created the detective Albert Campion?
   a) Margery Allingham
   b) Gladys Mitchell
   c) John Creasey

4) In which town are Ellis Peters's medieval murder mysteries featuring Brother Cadfael largely set?
   a) York
   b) Shrewsbury
   c) Winchester

5) Which American crime writer published an autobiography called *My Dark Places* in which he wrote about his own investigations into the murder of his mother?
   a) James Lee Burke
   b) Elmore Leonard
   c) James Ellroy

6) In which year was the first Sherlock Holmes story published?
   a) 1887
   b) 1890
   c) 1894

7) Under what pseudonym did cousins Frederic Dannay and Manfred B. Lee write crime fiction?
   a) Rex Stout
   b) Ellery Queen
   c) Erle Stanley Gardner

EXPERT

8) What is the name of Lord Peter Wimsey's valet in the detective novels written by Dorothy L. Sayers?
   a) Bunter
   b) Lugg
   c) Hastings

9) Who created the Chicago-based woman private eye V. I. Warshawski?
   a) Patricia Cornwell
   b) Sue Grafton
   c) Sara Paretsky

10) What is the Christian name of Georges Simenon's detective, Inspector Maigret?
   a) Charles
   b) Jules
   c) Georges

Answers: 1c, 2b, 3a, 4b, 5c, 6a, 7b, 8a, 9c, 10b

FICTIONAL CHARACTERS

In which well-known novels do the following characters appear:

EXPERT

1) **Michael Henchard**
   a) Joseph Conrad's *The Secret Agent*
   b) Kingsley Amis's *The Old Devils*
   c) Thomas Hardy's *The Mayor of Casterbridge*

2) **Isabel Archer**
   a) Charlotte Bronte's *The Professor*
   b) Virginia Woolf's *The Waves*
   c) Henry James's *The Portrait of a Lady*

3) **Lady Catherine de Bourgh**
   a) W. M. Thackeray's *Vanity Fair*
   b) Jane Austen's *Pride and Prejudice*
   c) Charles Dickens's *Great Expectations*

4) **Stephen Wraysford**
   a) Sebastian Faulks's *Birdsong*
   b) Nick Hornby's *About a Boy*
   c) Ian McEwan's *Enduring Love*

5) **Charles Ryder**
   a) Graham Greene's *Brighton Rock*
   b) Evelyn Waugh's *Brideshead Revisited*
   c) Iris Murdoch's *The Bell*

6) **Hester Prynne**
   a) Nathaniel Hawthorne's *The Scarlet Letter*
   b) Harriet Beecher Stowe's *Uncle Tom's Cabin*
   c) Charles Dickens's *David Copperfield*

7) **Christabel La Motte**
   a) Iris Murdoch's *The Sea, The Sea*
   b) A. S. Byatt's *Possession*
   c) Margaret Atwood's *Alias Grace*

8) **Augustus Melmotte**
   a) Oscar Wilde's *The Picture of Dorian Gray*
   b) George Eliot's *Middlemarch*
   c) Anthony Trollope's *The Way We Live Now*

9) **Sherman McCoy**
   a) Tom Wolfe's *The Bonfire of the Vanities*
   b) Bret Easton Ellis's *American Psycho*
   c) Saul Bellow's *Humboldt's Gift*

10) **Captain Cuttle**
   a) Charles Dickens's *Dombey and Son*
   b) R. L. Stevenson's *Treasure Island*
   c) C. S. Forester's *The African Queen*

EXPERT

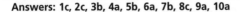

Answers: 1c, 2c, 3b, 4a, 5b, 6a, 7b, 8c, 9a, 10a

FICTIONAL PLACES

1) Which writer created an imaginary land at the centre of the earth's core called Pellucidar?
   a) Edgar Rice Burroughs
   b) Edgar Allan Poe
   c) Edgar Wallace

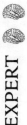

EXPERT

2) Which school did fictional fat boy Billy Bunter attend?
   a) Blackfriars
   b) Whitefriars
   c) Greyfriars

3) Which famous novelist collaborated with her brother, when they were children, to create the imaginary kingdom of Angria?
   a) Charlotte Brontë
   b) George Eliot
   c) Jane Austen

4) Who wrote a series of novels set on a desert planet called Arrakis?
   a) Ray Bradbury
   b) Isaac Asimov
   c) Frank Herbert

5) What was the name of the land of giants visited by Gulliver in Jonathan Swift's *Gulliver's Travels*?
   a) Laputa
   b) Brobdingnag
   c) Gargantua

6) Who wrote the satire *Erewhon* in which the narrator travels to a remote land of that name?
   a) William Morris
   b) Mark Twain
   c) Samuel Butler

7) What is the name of the town in which Ruth Rendell's Chief Inspector Wexford works?
   a) Kingsmarkham
   b) St. Mary Mead
   c) Arkham

8) Which writer created Lake Wobegon, Minnesota?
   a) Garrison Keillor
   b) James Thurber
   c) Thornton Wilder

9) In which city does Thomas Hardy's character Jude the Obscure hope to attend the university?
   a) Casterbridge
   b) Melchester
   c) Christminster

10) Rudolf Rassendyll impersonates the king of which Central European nation in Anthony Hope's novel *The Prisoner of Zenda*?
   a) Sylvania
   b) Ruritania
   c) Molvania

EXPERT

Answers: 1a, 2c, 3a, 4c, 5b, 6c, 7a, 8a, 9c, 10b

GENERAL LITERATURE 1

1) Who was the author of *Madame Bovary*?
   a) Honoré de Balzac
   b) Guy de Maupassant
   c) Gustave Flaubert

2) Which of Charles Dickens' novels was not made into a film in the 1940s?
   a) Martin Chuzzlewit
   b) Oliver Twist
   c) Great Expectations

3) Which Irish dramatist wrote *The Playboy of the Western World*?
   a) W. B. Yeats
   b) Sean O'Casey
   c) J. M. Synge

4) Which poet's verse translation of *Beowulf* received critical acclaim in 2000?
   a) Seamus Heaney
   b) Simon Armitage
   c) Andrew Motion

5) Who is the narrator of the Brer Rabbit stories, written by Joel Chandler Harris?
   a) Brer Rabbit
   b) Uncle Remus
   c) Uncle Joel

NOVICE

6) Who wrote the war trilogy *Men at Arms*?
   a) Ernest Hemingway
   b) C. S. Forester
   c) Evelyn Waugh

7) What nationality was the playwright August Strindberg?
   a) Swedish
   b) Norwegian
   c) German

8) From which literary work does the expression 'The Slough of Despond' originate?
   a) *Hamlet* by William Shakespeare
   b) *The Pilgrim's Progress* by John Bunyan
   c) *Paradise Lost* by John Milton

9) In which century was the poet Alexander Pope born?
   a) 17th
   b) 18th
   c) 19th

10) Who wrote the novel *A House for Mr Biswas*?
   a) Salman Rushdie
   b) V. S. Naipaul
   c) Vikram Seth

NOVICE

Answers: 1c, 2a, 3c, 4a, 5b, 6c, 7a, 8b, 9a, 10b

GENERAL LITERATURE 2

EXPERT

1) For which work is the medieval writer William Langland best known?
   a) *Piers Plowman*
   b) *Ancrene Wisse*
   c) *The Owl and the Nightingale*

2) In which novel by Sir Walter Scott does Jeanie Deans appear?
   a) *The Bride of Lammermoor*
   b) *The Heart of Midlothian*
   c) *Peveril of the Peak*

3) Which German novelist won the Nobel Prize for Literature in 1999?
   a) Günter Grass
   b) Thomas Mann
   c) Heinrich Böll

4) In Dostoevsky's novel, how many Brothers Karamazov are there?
   a) 2
   b) 3
   c) 4

5) In which of Chekhov's plays do we meet the character Vershinin?
   a) *The Three Sisters*
   b) *The Cherry Orchard*
   c) *Uncle Vanya*

6) Which French dramatist wrote *La Malade Imaginaire*?

  a) Jean-Baptiste Molière

  b) Jean Anouilh

  c) Jean Racine

7) Which comic writer created the character of Walter Mitty?

  a) P. G. Wodehouse

  b) Stephen Leacock

  c) James Thurber

8) What is the name of Sherlock Holmes's elder brother?

  a) Ashcroft

  b) Mycroft

  c) Sancroft

EXPERT

9) What do Malory's *Morte d'Arthur*, Bunyan's *The Pilgrim's Progress* and Adolf Hitler's *Mein Kampf* have in common?

  a) Each was the author's only book

  b) They were all written in prison

  c) They were all published without the author's knowledge

10) Who wrote an unfinished novel called *Sanditon*?

  a) Jane Austen

  b) George Eliot

  c) Charlotte Brontë

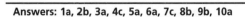

Answers: 1a, 2b, 3a, 4c, 5a, 6a, 7c, 8b, 9b, 10a

GENERAL LITERATURE 3

1) What kind of creature is Archie in *Archie and Mehitabel* by Don Marquis?
   a) An alley cat
   b) A cockroach
   c) A boll weevil

2) Which of these titles is not a novel by Neville Shute?
   a) *The Twyborn Affair*
   b) *A Town Like Alice*
   c) *Beyond the Black Stump*

3) In which of Ibsen's plays is the main character killed by a fall from a spire?
   a) *An Enemy of the People*
   b) *The Wild Duck*
   c) *The Master Builder*

4) Which novelist also wrote the lyrics for the song *Just My Bill* in *Showboat*?
   a) F. Scott Fitzgerald
   b) Len Deighton
   c) P. G. Wodehouse

5) Which of Brendan Behan's plays is set in a prison?
   a) *The Quare Fellow*
   b) *The Hostage*
   c) *Richard's Cork Leg*

6) Which well-known British novelist once played Ken Barlow's girlfriend in an episode of *Coronation Street*?
   a) Beryl Bainbridge
   b) Margaret Drabble
   c) Margaret Forster

7) Which of the following women writers was born in Wellington, New Zealand?
   a) Iris Murdoch
   b) Katherine Mansfield
   c) Muriel Spark

EXPERT

8) Who was the youngest of the Brontë sisters?
   a) Emily
   b) Charlotte
   c) Anne

9) Which Caribbean writer's major poetic work is the epic *Omeros* which is based on Homer's *Iliad* and *Odyssey*?
   a) Derek Walcott
   b) Grace Nichols
   c) John Agard

10) Which of George Bernard Shaw's plays, written in 1893, was banned by the censor and not produced for public performance until 1925?
   a) *Man and Superman*
   b) *Androcles and the Lion*
   c) *Mrs. Warren's Profession*

Answers: 1b, 2a, 3c, 4c, 5a, 6a, 7b, 8c, 9a, 10c

KIDS' BOOKS 1

EXPERT

1) Who created the character Tracy Beaker?
   a) Jacqueline Wilson
   b) Judy Blume
   c) Robin Klein

2) The children's classic *Heidi* is set in beautiful Alpine scenery in which country?
   a) Switzerland
   b) Germany
   c) Austria

3) Which fictional twelve-year-old has been described as 'the most ingenious criminal mastermind in history'?
   a) Artemis Fowl
   b) Harry Potter
   c) Adrian Mole

4) Who wrote *A Little Princess* and *The Secret Garden*?
   a) Edith Nesbit
   b) Frances Hodgson Burnett
   c) Enid Blyton

5) In the stories of Beatrix Potter, what kind of animal is Mr Tod?
   a) A fox
   b) A badger
   c) A toad

6) In which Roald Dahl book do we meet the Centipede, Old-Green-Grasshopper and Miss Spider?

   a) *Matilda*

   b) *The Witches*

   c) *James and the Giant Peach*

7) Kenneth Grahame wrote the original book *The Wind in the Willows* but it was later turned into a play *Toad of Toad Hall* by another famous writer for children. Who wrote this adaptation?

   a) A. A. Milne

   b) Enid Blyton

   c) C. S. Lewis

8) Who wrote the classic children's ballet story *Ballet Shoes*?

   a) Elinor Brent-Dyer

   b) Edith Nesbit

   c) Noel Streatfeild

9) Who catalogues *A Series of Unfortunate Events* in the lives of the Baudelaire children?

   a) Roald Dahl

   b) Eoin Colfer

   c) Lemony Snicket

10) In which book of Philip Pullman's trilogy *His Dark Materials* do Lyra and Will first meet?

   a) *Northern Lights*

   b) *The Subtle Knife*

   c) *The Amber Spyglass*

EXPERT

Answers: 1a, 2a, 3a, 4b, 5a, 6c, 7a, 8c, 9c, 10b

KIDS' BOOKS 2

1) Which character in children's fiction was created by Jean de Brunhoff?
   a) Tintin
   b) Babar the Elephant
   c) Matilda

2) Which two children feature in the stories by Rudyard Kipling entitled *Puck of Pook's Hill*?
   a) Peter and Lucy
   b) Dan and Una
   c) Mowgli and Kim

3) Which book by Alan Garner tells the story of how four children use three magical treasures to save a mysterious king and his land from evil?
   a) *The Weirdstone of Brisingamen*
   b) *The Moon of Gomrath*
   c) *Elidor*

4) How is Theodor S. Geisel better known?
   a) Hergé
   b) Captain W. E. Johns
   c) Dr Seuss

5) In *The Lion, The Witch and The Wardrobe*, the arrival of which character heralds the end of the Winter of the White Witch?
   a) Mr Tumnus the Fawn
   b) Father Christmas
   c) Aslan the Lion

GENIUS

6) In *Little Women* by Lousia M. Alcott, whom does Laurie eventually marry?
   a) Amy
   b) Beth
   c) Jo

7) In Terry Pratchett's *Discworld*, where do the Gods live?
   a) Dunmanifestin, a marble castle on top of a high mountain
   b) They are hidden in the Unseen University in Ankh Morpork
   c) In The Temple of the Gods in Ephebe, surrounded by a labyrinth

8) In *The Hobbit*, who kills Smaug the Dragon?
   a) Bilbo Baggins
   b) Thorin Oakenshield
   c) Bard the Bowman

9) In the 'William' books by Richmal Crompton, what is William's surname?
   a) Brown
   b) Black
   c) White

10) In which of J. K. Rowling's Harry Potter series does the Triwizard Tournament take place?
   a) *Harry Potter and the Philosopher's Stone*
   b) *Harry Potter and the Prisoner of Azkaban*
   c) *Harry Potter and the Goblet of Fire*

GENIUS

Answers: 1b, 2b, 3c, 4c, 5b, 6a, 7a, 8c, 9a, 10c

NOVELS AND NOVELISTS 1

NOVICE

1) Who wrote the novels *Birdsong* and *Charlotte Gray*?
   a) Sebastian Faulks
   b) Ian McEwan
   c) Louis de Bernières

2) Which novel did Dickens leave unfinished at his death?
   a) *Dombey and Son*
   b) *Our Mutual Friend*
   c) *The Mystery of Edwin Drood*

3) What is the surname of Emma in Jane Austen's novel of that name?
   a) Woodhouse
   b) Dashwood
   c) Bennett

4) In which novel does a pivotal incident take place in the Malabar Caves?
   a) *Lord of the Flies* by William Golding
   b) *Midnight's Children* by Salman Rushdie
   c) *A Passage to India* by E. M. Forster

5) Who wrote *The Color Purple*?
   a) Toni Morrison
   b) Alice Walker
   c) Joyce Carol Oates

6) What is the name of the house to which the narrator is taken by her new husband in Daphne Du Maurier's novel *Rebecca*?
   a) Pemberley
   b) Manderley
   c) Menabilly

7) Which classic novel has the alternative title of *The Modern Prometheus*?
   a) Mary Shelley's *Frankenstein*
   b) R. L. Stevenson's *Dr. Jekyll and Mr. Hyde*
   c) Bram Stoker's *Dracula*

8) How was Eleanor Hibbert better known to fans of historical romances?
   a) Jean Plaidy
   b) Georgette Heyer
   c) Edith Pargeter

9) Which novel won the Pulitzer Prize for Fiction in 1937?
   a) F. Scott Fitzgerald's *The Great Gatsby*
   b) John Steinbeck's *The Grapes of Wrath*
   c) Margaret Mitchell's *Gone with the Wind*

10) In which novel does a character called Billy Pilgrim survive the fire-bombing of Dresden in World War II?
   a) Kurt Vonnegut's *Slaughterhouse-5*
   b) Joseph Heller's *Catch-22*
   c) John O'Hara's *Butterfield 8*

NOVICE

Answers: 1a, 2c, 3a, 4c, 5b, 6b, 7a, 8a, 9c, 10a

NOVELS AND NOVELISTS 2

EXPERT

1) **Which of Dickens's heroines marries Bentley Drummle?**
   a) Little Nell in *The Old Curiosity Shop*
   b) Esther Summerson in *Bleak House*
   c) Estella in *Great Expectations*

2) **Who wrote the Booker Prize-winning novel *The Remains of the Day*?**
   a) Kazuo Ishiguro
   b) Michael Ondaatje
   c) Salman Rushdie

3) **What is the first name of the gamekeeper Mellors in D. H. Lawrence's *Lady Chatterley's Lover*?**
   a) Oliver
   b) Roger
   c) Rupert

4) **Which 19th century novelist published sketches and essays under the pseudonym Michael Angelo Titmarsh?**
   a) Charles Dickens
   b) W. M. Thackeray
   c) Thomas Hardy

5) **Other than Jim Hawkins, who else narrates Robert Louis Stevenson's *Treasure Island*?**
   a) Long John Silver
   b) Dr Livesey
   c) Squire Trelawney

6) Which Thomas Hardy novel tells the story of the love affair between Dick Dewey and Fancy Day?
   a) *The Woodlanders*
   b) *Under the Greenwood Tree*
   c) *The Trumpet Major*

7) Which Australian novelist won the Nobel Prize for Literature in 1973?
   a) Thomas Keneally
   b) Patrick White
   c) Christina Stead

8) Which classic novel was inspired by the real-life adventures of Alexander Selkirk?
   a) *Rob Roy* by Sir Walter Scott
   b) *Kidnapped* by Robert Louis Stevenson
   c) *Robinson Crusoe* by Daniel Defoe

9) Who wrote the novels *Alias Grace* and *Oryx and Crake*?
   a) A. S. Byatt
   b) Margaret Atwood
   c) Jeanette Winterson

10) What is the profession of Adam Bede in the novel of the same name by George Eliot?
   a) Lawyer
   b) Carpenter
   c) Clergyman

EXPERT

Answers: 1c, 2a, 3a, 4b, 5b, 6b, 7b, 8c, 9b, 10b

POETRY 1

1) In 1995, the poem *If* was voted the nation's favourite poem. Who was the author?
   a) Alfred Lord Tennyson
   b) Rudyard Kipling
   c) Robert Browning

2) Which 20th century poet's autobiography is entitled *Summoned by Bells*?
   a) John Betjeman
   b) Wilfred Owen
   c) W. H. Auden

3) In *The Pied Piper of Hamelin* what kind of creatures did the piper spirit away?
   a) Rats and mice
   b) Rats and children
   c) Rats and the Town Council

4) Whose *Revolting Rhymes* are popular with young readers?
   a) Lewis Carroll
   b) Roald Dahl
   c) Roger McGough

5) Which poem features the death of an albatross?
   a) *Sea Fever* by John Masefield
   b) *Dover Beach* by Matthew Arnold
   c) *The Rime of the Ancient Mariner* by Samuel Taylor Coleridge

NOVICE

6) Who compared his lover to a summer's day?
   a) William Shakespeare
   b) Andrew Marvell
   c) Robert Burns

7) Who wrote the poems which are used in the lyrics for the Andrew Lloyd Webber musical *Cats*?
   a) Philip Larkin
   b) T. S. Eliot
   c) W. B. Yeats

NOVICE

8) Which of these poems was written by John Keats?
   a) *To a Skylark*
   b) *Ode to the West Wind*
   c) *Ode to a Nightingale*

9) Which poem opens with the line 'The Curfew tolls the knell of parting day'?
   a) *Elegy Written in a Country Churchyard* by Thomas Gray
   b) *On his Blindness* by John Milton
   c) *Composed upon Westminster Bridge, Sept 3, 1802* by William Wordsworth

10) Which poem by Lewis Carroll was used as the basis for a film by Terry Gilliam?
   a) *The Walrus and the Carpenter*
   b) *Jabberwocky*
   c) *The Hunting of the Snark*

Answers: 1b, 2a, 3b, 4b, 5c, 6a, 7b, 8c, 9a, 10b

POETRY 2

EXPERT

1) Which poem opens with the line 'Had we but world enough and time'?
   a) *The Passionate Shepherd to his Love* by Christopher Marlowe
   b) *To His Coy Mistress* by Andrew Marvell
   c) *To the Virgins, to Make Much of Time* by Robert Herrick

2) Which of these was one of the 'Lake Poets'?
   a) Robert Southey
   b) John Keats
   c) Dante Gabriel Rossetti

3) Which poet of the First World War wrote *Anthem for Doomed Youth*?
   a) Siegfried Sassoon
   b) Wilfred Owen
   c) Laurence Binyon

4) George Gordon, Lord Byron, was also Baron of where?
   a) Rochdale
   b) Rutland
   c) Rochester

5) Which writer, better known as a novelist, wrote the poems *Snake* and *Bavarian Gentians*?
   a) H. Rider Haggard
   b) D. H. Lawrence
   c) Thomas Hardy

6) Who wrote and published poems under the pseudonym 'Currer Bell'?
   a) Benjamin Disraeli
   b) Charles Dickens
   c) Charlotte Brontë

7) Roger McGough and Brian Patten are two of the Liverpool poets who started writing in the 1960s. Who was the third?
   a) Adrian Henri
   b) Adrian Mitchell
   c) Norman Nicholson

EXPERT

8) Who was the British Poet Laureate for 37 years, from 1930 to 1967?
   a) Robert Bridges
   b) John Masefield
   c) Cecil Day-Lewis

9) Which English county was celebrated by A. E. Housman?
   a) Cheshire
   b) Shropshire
   c) Staffordshire

10) Who was the author of the lament for a dead lover *Stop All the Clocks*, used in the film *Four Weddings and a Funeral*?
   a) Louis McNeice
   b) W. H. Auden
   c) John Betjeman

Answers: 1b, 2a, 3b, 4a, 5b, 6c, 7a, 8b, 9b, 10b

POETRY 3

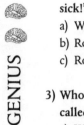

GENIUS

1) Which of Chaucer's *Canterbury Tales* features patient Griselda?
   a) *The Wife of Bath's Tale*
   b) *The Reeve's Prologue and Tale*
   c) *The Clerk's Prologue and Tale*

2) Who wrote the poem which begins 'O Rose, thou art sick!'?
   a) William Blake
   b) Robert Herrick
   c) Robert Burns

3) Who wrote: 'Death, be not proud, although some have called thee/Mighty and dreadful'?
   a) William Shakespeare
   b) John Donne
   c) John Milton

4) Who wrote the poem called *Not Waving but Drowning*?
   a) Stevie Smith
   b) Sylvia Plath
   c) Wendy Cope

5) Who is the author of these lines 'Be nice to yu turkeys dis christmas/Cos' turkeys just wanna hav fun'?
   a) Spike Milligan
   b) Benjamin Zephaniah
   c) Roger McGough

6) Which poet remembered Adlestrop?
   a) R. S. Thomas
   b) Edward Thomas
   c) Dylan Thomas

7) The poem *Abou Ben Adhem* was written in 1838 by whom?
   a) Leigh Hunt
   b) Alfred Austin
   c) Alfred, Lord Tennyson

8) Where was poet John Agard born?
   a) New Zealand
   b) Jamaica
   c) Guyana

9) Which was the relationship between Christina and Dante Gabriel Rossetti?
   a) Husband and wife
   b) Brother and sister
   c) Mother and son

10) To what was Thomas Wyatt the Elder most likely referring when he wrote: 'The bell tower showed me such sight/That in my head sticks day and night'?
   a) The execution of Anne Boleyn
   b) The funeral procession of Queen Elizabeth I
   c) The Great Fire of London

Answers: 1c, 2a, 3b, 4a, 5b, 6b, 7a, 8c, 9b, 10a

PSEUDONYMS

What were/are the real names behind the following writers' pseudonyms?

EXPERT

1) **James Herriot**
   a) James Alfred Wright
   b) James Alfred Wight
   c) James Alfred Knight

2) **Barbara Vine**
   a) Ruth Rendell
   b) Patricia Wentworth
   c) Patricia Cornwell

3) **O. Henry**
   a) William Cory
   b) William S. Porter
   c) Edwin Arlington Robinson

4) **Ellis Bell**
   a) Virginia Woolf
   b) Emily Brontë
   c) Jean Rhys

5) **Mary Westmacott**
   a) Dorothy L. Sayers
   b) Margery Allingham
   c) Agatha Christie

6) **Flann O'Brien**
   a) Brian O'Nolan
   b) Sean O'Casey
   c) Brian O'Flaherty

7) **Richard Bachman**
   a) Stephen King
   b) Clive Barker
   c) James Herbert

8) **Nicci French**
   a) Nicci Gerrard and Karl French
   b) Nicci Gerrard and Sean French
   c) Nicci Gerrard and Philip French

9) **Dan Kavanagh**
   a) Martin Amis
   b) Ian McEwan
   c) Julian Barnes

10) **Corno di Bassetto**
   a) George Bernard Shaw
   b) Oscar Wilde
   c) J. M. Barrie

EXPERT

Answers: 1b, 2a, 3b, 4b, 5c, 6a, 7a, 8b, 9c, 10a

QUOTATIONS

EXPERT

1) What did Peter Pan, in J. M. Barrie's play, describe as 'an awfully big adventure'?
   a) Life
   b) Death
   c) Love

2) Which footballer once remarked, cryptically, at a press conference, 'When the seagulls follow the trawler it's because they think sardines will be thrown into the sea'?
   a) Johann Cruyff
   b) Ruud Gullit
   c) Eric Cantona

3) Which comedian once said, 'I don't care to belong to any club that will have me as a member'?
   a) Woody Allen
   b) Charlie Chaplin
   c) Groucho Marx

4) Which general said of his soldiers, 'I don't know what effect these men will have upon the enemy but, by God, they terrify me'?
   a) Duke of Wellington
   b) Field Marshal Montgomery
   c) Napoleon

5) In which book has Great Aunt Ada Doom seen, 'Something nasty in the woodshed'?
   a) *Carry on, Jeeves* by P. G. Wodehouse
   b) *Cold Comfort Farm* by Stella Gibbons
   c) *Love in a Cold Climate* by Nancy Mitford

6) Of what did Dr Johnson say, 'There is nothing which has yet been contrived by man, by which so much happiness is produced'?
   a) A good book
   b) A good meal
   c) A good tavern

7) Of which film actress did Dorothy Parker write, 'She ran the whole gamut of her emotions from A to B'?
   a) Bette Davis
   b) Katherine Hepburn
   c) Joan Crawford

8) Of which politician did Denis Healey say that being attacked by him was like 'being savaged by a dead sheep'?
   a) Geoffrey Howe
   b) John Major
   c) William Whitelaw

EXPERT

9) What were reputed to be the last words of the artist J. M. W. Turner?
   a) 'I think I could eat one of Bellamy's veal pies'
   b) 'The sun is God'
   c) 'It has all been most interesting'

10) Who said, 'The only difference between me and a madman is that I'm not mad'?
   a) Salvador Dali
   b) Spike Milligan
   c) George III

Answers: 1b, 2c, 3c, 4a, 5b, 6c, 7b, 8a, 9b, 10a

SCIENCE FICTION AND FANTASY

EXPERT

1) Philip K. Dick's novel *Do Androids Dream of Electric Sheep* was the basis for which movie?
   a) *Silent Running*
   b) *Dark Star*
   c) *Blade Runner*

2) Which word or phrase is said to have been coined by William Gibson in his novel *Neuromancer*?
   a) Cyberspace
   b) Virtual reality
   c) Globalisation

3) Which writer developed the '3 Laws of Robotics'?
   a) Arthur C. Clarke
   b) Ray Bradbury
   c) Isaac Asimov

4) Which novelist created the character known as the Stainless Steel Rat?
   a) Isaac Asimov
   b) Harry Harrison
   c) Robert B. Heinlein

5) What eventually defeats the invading Martians in H. G. Wells's *The War of the Worlds*?
   a) Bacteria
   b) Fire
   c) Poisonous gas

6) Who wrote the Hugo Award-winning novel *The Left Hand of Darkness*?
   a) Orson Scott Card
   b) Ursula K. Le Guin
   c) Lois McMaster Bujold

7) In Stephen Donaldson's *Chronicles of Thomas Covenant*, from what disease does the central character suffer?
   a) Leprosy
   b) AIDS
   c) Cancer

8) Who is the author of *The Wheel of Time* sequence of fantasy novels?
   a) Robert Jordan
   b) David Eddings
   c) Tad Williams

9) What is the name given to the civilisation of super-beings imagined by Iain M. Banks in his novels?
   a) The Hive
   b) The Culture
   c) The Matrix

10) What does the C stand for in Arthur C. Clarke's name?
   a) Collins
   b) Clive
   c) Charles

EXPERT

Answers: 1c, 2a, 3c, 4b, 5a, 6b, 7a, 8a, 9b, 10c

SHAKESPEARE 1

NOVICE

1) Which play begins in Venice and then moves to Cyprus?
   a) *As You Like It*
   b) *Othello*
   c) *Measure for Measure*

2) 'I know thee not, old man. Fall to thy prayers.' Which King is speaking to Falstaff here?
   a) Henry IV
   b) Henry V
   c) Henry VI

3) Which Shakespearean tragedy ends with a speech by the Prince of Norway?
   a) *King Lear*
   b) *Hamlet*
   c) *Macbeth*

4) Which play has the subtitle, 'Or What You Will'?
   a) *Twelfth Night*
   b) *The Tempest*
   c) *Much Ado About Nothing*

5) In which play do the feuding lovers Beatrice and Benedick appear?
   a) *Love's Labour's Lost*
   b) *The Taming of the Shrew*
   c) *Much Ado About Nothing*

6) From which Shakespeare play did Aldous Huxley take the title of his novel *Brave New World*?
   a) *Hamlet*
   b) *The Tempest*
   c) *Othello*

7) *In Romeo and Juliet* who kills Tybalt?
   a) Mercutio
   b) Romeo
   c) Benvolio

8) Which of the following is not one of King Lear's daughters?
   a) Rosalind
   b) Regan
   c) Cordelia

9) Which Shakespeare play includes the famous stage direction, 'Exit, pursued by a bear'?
   a) *The Tempest*
   b) *All's Well That Ends Well*
   c) *The Winter's Tale*

10) A character called Portia appears in *The Merchant of Venice* and which other Shakespeare play?
   a) *Julius Caesar*
   b) *Antony and Cleopatra*
   c) *The Taming of the Shrew*

NOVICE

Answers: 1b, 2b, 3b, 4a, 5c, 6b, 7b, 8a, 9c, 10a

SHAKESPEARE 2

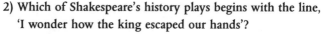

1) Which loving husband in a Shakespeare play refers to his wife as his 'dearest chuck'?
   a) Petruchio in *The Taming of the Shrew*
   b) Macbeth in *Macbeth*
   c) Romeo in *Romeo and Juliet*

2) Which of Shakespeare's history plays begins with the line, 'I wonder how the king escaped our hands'?
   a) *Henry VI Part 3*
   b) *Henry V*
   c) *Henry VI Part 1*

3) Which play has characters called Froth, Elbow and Mistress Overdone?
   a) *The Merry Wives of Windsor*
   b) *Measure for Measure*
   c) *Henry IV Part 1*

4) What was the name of Shakespeare's only son?
   a) Hamlet
   b) William
   c) Hamnet

5) Which Shakespearean hero has a mother, presumably a large lady, named Volumnia?
   a) Coriolanus
   b) Mark Antony
   c) Titus Andronicus

6) From which play does the line, 'The course of true love never did run smooth', come?
   a) *Romeo and Juliet*
   b) *Antony and Cleopatra*
   c) *A Midsummer Night's Dream*

7) In what year was the First Folio of Shakespeare's plays published?
   a) 1613
   b) 1623
   c) 1633

GENIUS

8) At which university had Hamlet been a student?
   a) Wittenberg
   b) Heidelberg
   c) Königsberg

9) What was the name of the house Shakespeare bought in his home town of Stratford-on-Avon in 1597?
   a) Avon House
   b) Church Manor
   c) New Place

10) Who, in a Shakespeare play, sings a song that begins, 'The woosel cock so black of hue…'?
    a) Bottom in *A Midsummer Night's Dream*
    b) Feste in *Twelfth Night*
    c) The Fool in *King Lear*

Answers: 1b, 2a, 3b, 4c, 5a, 6c, 7b, 8a, 9c, 10a

WEIRD WORDS

Which of the three definitions of the following words is the correct one?

GENIUS

1) **Dumbledore**
   a) A type of apple grown in Somerset
   b) A type of bee
   c) A wise old man

2) **Jobbernowl**
   a) A stupid person
   b) A printer's apprentice
   c) A ghost

3) **Badious**
   a) Chestnut-coloured
   b) Relating to a spa
   c) Mischievous

4) **Debellate**
   a) To cut off someone's head
   b) To cut down trees
   c) To conquer in war

5) **Aulete**
   a) A servant
   b) An ancient Greek flautist
   c) A gold bracelet

6) Tomium
   a) A compliment
   b) The cutting edge of a bird's bill
   c) A small drum

7) Lampadephore
   a) A torchbearer
   b) A collector of lamps
   c) A system of signalling using lights

8) Mundungus
   a) An Australian wild dog
   b) A type of large, drooping moustache
   c) A form of cheap, foul-smelling tobacco

GENIUS

9) Fimbriated
   a) Under the influence of drink
   b) Having a border or fringe
   c) Shaped like a fish's tail

10) Pastinaceous
   a) Relating to the parsnip
   b) Impertinent
   c) Having a bread-like consistency

Answers: 1b, 2a, 3a, 4c, 5b, 6b, 7a, 8c, 9b, 10a

WORDS

1) From which language do we get the word 'bungalow'?
   a) Bengali
   b) Portuguese
   c) Gujarati

2) What is a paronomosia?
   a) A play on words
   b) A logical contradiction
   c) A verbal exaggeration

GENIUS

3) To what animal does the adjective 'hircine' refer?
   a) Deer
   b) Sheep
   c) Goat

4) Which writer invented the word 'frabjous' in one of his poems?
   a) William Blake
   b) Edward Lear
   c) Lewis Carroll

5) What does a deltiologist collect?
   a) Cigarette cards
   b) Postcards
   c) Football programmes

6) To what animal does the word 'murine' refer?
   a) Beaver
   b) Squirrel
   c) Mouse

7) From which language do we get the word 'yacht'?
   a) Dutch
   b) German
   c) Swedish

8) If something is described as 'helminthoid', what shape is it?
   a) Shield-shaped
   b) Worm-shaped
   c) Arrow-shaped

9) What is an 'oxymoron'?
   a) A contradiction in terms
   b) A type of semi-colon
   c) A rhetorical proclamation

10) From which language do we get the word 'algebra'?
   a) Bengali
   b) Arabic
   c) Greek

GENIUS

Answers: 1a, 2a, 3c, 4c, 5b, 6c, 7a, 8b, 9a, 10b

MUSIC
AND THE
ARTS

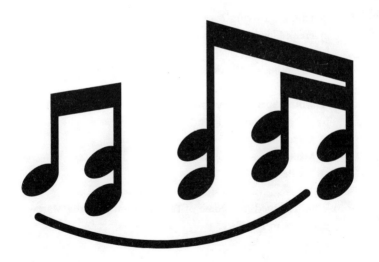

ARCHITECTURE

EXPERT

1) Which architects designed the Houses of Parliament in Westminster, completed in 1860?
   a) Sir Charles Barry and Augustus Pugin
   b) Augustus Pugin and Sir George Gilbert Scott
   c) Sir Charles Barry and Sir George Gilbert Scott

2) Which of the following landmark 20th century buildings was designed by the Danish architect Jorn Utzon?
   a) The Pompidou Centre
   b) Lloyd's of London Building
   c) Sydney Opera House

3) Which architect created the concept of a house as a 'machine for living'?
   a) Frank Lloyd Wright
   b) Norman Foster
   c) Le Corbusier (Charles Edouard Jeanneret)

4) In which Spanish city can nearly all the buildings designed by Antoni Gaudi be found?
   a) Barcelona
   b) Madrid
   c) Seville

5) Who designed the Dome of the cathedral of Santa Maria del Fiore in Florence?
   a) Michelangelo
   b) Brunelleschi
   c) Raphael

6) Which of the following buildings was designed by Sir Christopher Wren?
   a) The library at Trinity College, Cambridge
   b) Christ Church, Spitalfields
   c) Blenheim Palace

7) Which Roman author wrote *Ten Books on Architecture*, a work which has continued to influence Western architecture through the centuries?
   a) Cicero
   b) Vitruvius
   c) Columella

8) Where in Europe is the Guggenheim Museum, designed by Frank Gehry?
   a) Vienna
   b) Stockholm
   c) Bilbao

9) Who designed the National Theatre, London?
   a) Sir Denys Lasdun
   b) Sir Norman Foster
   c) Sir Richard Rogers

10) Which Mughal emperor of India commissioned the Taj Mahal as a mausoleum for his wife?
   a) Aurangzeb
   b) Babur
   c) Shah Jahan

Answers: 1a, 2c, 3c, 4a, 5b, 6a, 7b, 8c, 9a, 10c

EXPERT

ART AND ARTISTS 1

1) Who painted *The Night Watch*?
   a) Rubens
   b) Rembrandt
   c) Renoir

2) Which artist did the 19th century critic John Ruskin accuse of 'flinging a pot of paint in the public's face'?
   a) Whistler
   b) Turner
   c) Monet

3) Which world-renowned sculpture was created by Frederic-Auguste Bartholdi?
   a) The Statue of Liberty
   b) The Burghers of Calais
   c) The Thinker

4) Which 20th century American artist was born Emmanuel Radnitzky?
   a) Mark Rothko
   b) Jasper Johns
   c) Man Ray

5) Which Italian artist fled Rome in 1606 because he had killed a man in an argument over a game of tennis?
   a) Correggio
   b) Caravaggio
   c) Canaletto

6) Which Italian artist had a name that means 'little barrel'?
   a) Modigliani
   b) Donatello
   c) Botticelli

7) Who painted *Girl with a Pearl Earring*?
   a) Vermeer
   b) Van Gogh
   c) Van Dyck

8) Which of the following painters was not a founder member of the Pre-Raphaelite Brotherhood?
   a) Sir John Millais
   b) William Holman Hunt
   c) Sir Edward Burne-Jones

9) What animal is suspended in a glass tank of formaldehyde in Damien Hirst's work *The Physical Impossibility of Death in the Mind of Someone Living*?
   a) A sheep
   b) A cow
   c) A shark

10) With which art movement is the French artist Georges Seurat principally associated?
   a) Pointillism
   b) Fauvism
   c) Expressionism

NOVICE

Answers: 1b, 2a, 3a, 4c, 5b, 6c, 7a, 8c, 9c, 10a

ART AND ARTISTS 2

1) Which 18th century French artist painted a picture entitled
   The Swing?
   a) Fragonard
   b) Boucher
   c) Watteau

2) Which Italian painter's name (given as a nickname) means
   'oxhead' in English?
   a) Giotto
   b) Uccello
   c) Cimabue

3) With which 20th century art movement is the painter Roy
   Lichtenstein chiefly associated?
   a) Surrealism
   b) Abstract Expressionism
   c) Pop Art

4) In which town did the Dutch artist Jan Vermeer live and
   work all his life?
   a) Amsterdam
   b) Delft
   c) Leiden

5) Who played the abstract expressionist painter Jackson
   Pollock in the 2000 movie *Pollock*?
   a) Ed Harris
   b) Brad Pitt
   c) Val Kilmer

EXPERT

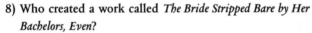

6) For what subject is the 18th century English artist George Stubbs most famous?
   a) Mermaids
   b) Horses
   c) Matchstick men

7) On which Mediterranean island was El Greco born?
   a) Crete
   b) Malta
   c) Rhodes

EXPERT

8) Who created a work called *The Bride Stripped Bare by Her Bachelors, Even*?
   a) Max Ernst
   b) Damien Hirst
   c) Marcel Duchamp

9) Which French artist drew Marie Antoinette as she was on her way to the guillotine?
   a) Jacques-Louis David
   b) Jean-Auguste-Dominique Ingres
   c) Eugene Delacroix

10) Which of the following is a name given to a group of 19th century American artists?
    a) The Hudson River School
    b) The Missouri River School
    c) The East River School

Answers: 1a, 2c, 3c, 4b, 5a, 6b, 7a, 8c, 9a, 10a

ART AND ARTISTS 3

1) In which year did Picasso die?
   a) 1963
   b) 1973
   c) 1983

2) Which 19th century French artist painted *The Gleaners*?
   a) Theodore Gericault
   b) Jean Francois Millet
   c) Gustave Courbet

3) Which painter won the first Turner Prize in 1984?
   a) Howard Hodgkin
   b) Malcolm Morley
   c) Chris Ofili

4) With which art movement is Bridget Riley most associated?
   a) Op Art
   b) Dadaism
   c) Cubism

5) In which century was the Italian painter Giotto born?
   a) 12th
   b) 13th
   c) 14th

EXPERT

6) Who created a sculpture called *The Little Dancer*?
   a) Jacob Epstein
   b) Auguste Rodin
   c) Edgar Degas

7) In which country was the 20th century painter Marc Chagall born?
   a) Germany
   b) France
   c) Russia

8) Which of the following is not the name of a 20th century art movement?
   a) Vorticism
   b) Resistentialism
   c) Rayonism

9) Which of the following French artists worked for most of his life as a customs inspector?
   a) Paul Gauguin
   b) Henri Rousseau
   c) Claude Monet

10) Which 20th century American artist painted a work entitled *Nighthawks*?
   a) Edward Hopper
   b) Georgia O'Keeffe
   c) Grant Wood

EXPERT

Answers: 1b, 2b, 3b, 4a, 5b, 6c, 7c, 8b, 9b, 10a

CLASSICAL MUSIC 1

EXPERT

1) Who was the composer of the three piano pieces known as *Gymnopédies?*
   a) Maurice Ravel
   b) Claude Debussy
   c) Erik Satie

2) Beethoven used the words of which poet for the *Ode to Joy* in his 9th symphony?
   a) Goethe
   b) Heine
   c) Schiller

3) Who wrote the oratorio *Balshazzar's Feast?*
   a) Edward Elgar
   b) William Walton
   c) Ralph Vaughan Williams

4) How many movements did Schubert complete in his Symphony No. 8 in B Minor, known as the *Unfinished Symphony?*
   a) 1
   b) 2
   c) 3

5) Who wrote a String Quartet in F major, Op. 96, known as the *American*?
   a) Samuel Barber
   b) Anton Dvorák
   c) Leonard Bernstein

6) How is Beethoven's Piano Sonata No. 14 in C-sharp Minor Opus 27, No. 2 better known?
   a) *The Moonlight Sonata*
   b) *The Appassionata Sonata*
   c) *The Waldstein Sonata*

7) Which well-known composition includes pieces called *In the Hall of the Mountain King* and *Anitra's Song*?
   a) Prokofiev's *Peter and the Wolf*
   b) Mussorgsky's *Pictures at an Exhibition*
   c) Grieg's *Peer Gynt Suite*

8) Which Italian Renaissance composer was also Prince of Venosa and arranged to have his adulterous wife and her lover murdered?
   a) Palestrina
   b) Gesualdo
   c) Gabrieli

9) Which 19th century French composer wrote a *Song of the Railways*?
   a) Berlioz
   b) Gounod
   c) Fauré

10) What nationality was the 20th century composer Arthur Honegger?
   a) German
   b) French
   c) Austrian

EXPERT

Answers: 1c, 2c, 3b, 4b, 5b, 6a, 7c, 8b, 9a, 10b

CLASSICAL MUSIC 2

1) Which American composer wrote the piece *El Salon Mexico*?
   a) Samuel Barber
   b) Leonard Bernstein
   c) Aaron Copland

2) Which of Benjamin Britten's works was based on tunes that he had written as a child?
   a) *A Young Person's Guide to the Orchestra*
   b) *Simple Symphony Opus No. 4*
   c) *A Time There Was*

3) Which composer wrote *The Symphony of Sorrowful Songs*?
   a) Sergei Prokofiev
   b) Alexander Glazunov
   c) Henryk Gorecki

4) To whom was Beethoven's group of three string quartets, Opus 59, dedicated?
   a) Count Razumovsky
   b) Archduke Rudolph of Austria
   c) Baron van Swieten

5) Which work by Schubert tells the story of a child whose soul is stolen by a supernatural being?
   a) *Der Tod und das Mädchen*
   b) *Der Erl-König*
   c) *Die Schöne Müllerin*

GENIUS

6) Leoš Janáček's *Glagolitic Mass* requires choirs to sing in which language?
   a) Serbo-Croat
   b) Old Slavonic
   c) Latin

7) Whose choral work *Springtime in Funen* celebrates his homeland?
   a) Jean Sibelius
   b) Carl Nielsen
   c) Edvard Grieg

8) Who composed the incidental music to Alphonse Daudet's play *L'Arlésienne*?
   a) Claude Debussy
   b) Gabriel Fauré
   c) Georges Bizet

9) Who was the original composer of the cello solo known as *The Dying Swan* which was choreographed by Fokine and danced by Anna Pavlova?
   a) Pyotr Ilyitch Tchaikovsky
   b) Léo Delibes
   c) Camille Saint-Saëns

10) *The Arrival of the Queen of Sheba* is taken from which of Handel's oratorios?
    a) *Israel in Egypt*
    b) *Semele*
    c) *Solomon*

Answers: 1c, 2b, 3c, 4a, 5b, 6b, 7b, 8c, 9c, 10c

GENIUS

CLASSICAL MUSIC 3

1) **Who is the patron saint of music?**
   a) St. Christopher
   b) St. Cecilia
   c) St. Catherine

2) **Who composed the *Warsaw Concerto*?**
   a) Richard Addinsell
   b) Frederic Chopin
   c) Eric Coates

EXPERT

3) **Which British composer wrote *The Dream of Gerontius*?**
   a) Benjamin Britten
   b) Ralph Vaughan Williams
   c) Edward Elgar

4) **In which city was Antonio Vivaldi born?**
   a) Venice
   b) Naples
   c) Rome

5) **In Gustav Holst's *The Planets Suite* which planet is described as 'the bringer of jollity'?**
   a) Saturn
   b) Jupiter
   c) Neptune

6) Which Russian composer wrote the score for Sergei Eisenstein's film *Alexander Nevsky*?
   a) Stravinsky
   b) Shostakovich
   c) Prokofiev

7) The music of which composer, according to Mark Twain, was 'better than it sounds'?
   a) Wagner
   b) Richard Strauss
   c) Beethoven

8) What name is usually given to Mozart's Symphony No. 41 in C Major?
   a) *The Paris Symphony*
   b) *The Jupiter Symphony*
   c) *The Prague Symphony*

9) Who wrote the *Academic Festival Overture*?
   a) Beethoven
   b) Brahms
   c) Berlioz

10) By what name is the 20th century English composer Philip Heseltine better known?
   a) George Butterworth
   b) Constant Lambert
   c) Peter Warlock

EXPERT

Answers: 1b, 2a, 3c, 4a, 5b, 6c, 7a, 8b, 9b, 10c

DANCE

1) What was the real name of the ballerina Alicia Markova?
   a) Alicia Marks
   b) Alice Marx
   c) Lillian Markstein

2) From which country does the dance called the 'csardas' come?
   a) Russia
   b) Poland
   c) Hungary

GENIUS

3) Who wrote the music for the ballet *Coppélia*?
   a) Claude Debussy
   b) Léo Delibes
   c) Pyotr Tchaikovsky

4) What was the name of the great choreographer who choreographed the first performances of Tchaikovsky's ballets *Swan Lake* and *The Sleeping Beauty*?
   a) Jules Perrot
   b) Marius Petipa
   c) Arthur Saint-Leon

5) In which ballet do the characters Count Albrecht and Hilarion appear?
   a) *Giselle*
   b) *Swan Lake*
   c) *Coppélia*

6) Which pioneer of modern dance died when her long headscarf was caught on the wheel of her car?
   a) Isadora Duncan
   b) Twyla Tharp
   c) Martha Graham

7) Which well-known 20th century dancer was born Frederick Austerlitz?
   a) Sir Frederick Ashton
   b) Anton Dolin
   c) Fred Astaire

8) Who took the role of the dancer Victoria Page in the 1948 Powell and Pressburger film *The Red Shoes*?
   a) Moira Shearer
   b) Margot Fonteyn
   c) Margaret Lockwood

9) In which year did Rudolf Nureyev defect from Russia to the West?
   a) 1961
   b) 1964
   c) 1969

10) How does the waltz get its name?
   a) From the small Austrian town of Waltz where it originated
   b) From Friedrich von Waltz who was the first composer to write waltzes
   c) From the German word 'waltzen', meaning to revolve

Answers: 1a, 2c, 3b, 4b, 5a, 6a, 7c, 8a, 9a, 10c

EIGHTIES MUSIC

1) Who won the Eurovision Song Contest in 1988?
   a) Bucks Fizz
   b) Sandra Kim
   c) Céline Dion

2) Of which 1980s group were Siobhan Fahey and Keren Woodward members?
   a) The Bangles
   b) Bananarama
   c) Spandau Ballet

3) What was Abba's last UK No. 1, released in 1980?
   a) *Take a Chance on Me*
   b) *Knowing Me, Knowing You*
   c) *Super Trouper*

4) Who had a hit in 1988 with *Orinoco Flow*?
   a) Tiffany
   b) Enya
   c) Sonya

5) Who sang the theme song for the 1987 Bond movie *The Living Daylights*?
   a) A-Ha
   b) Duran Duran
   c) Sheena Easton

NOVICE

6) How did the 1980s group Bronski Beat get its name?
   a) Its members admired a Russian revolutionary called Leonid Bronski
   b) Its keyboard player was called Steve Bronski
   c) It was an anagram of the initials of the band members

7) With which group did Lionel Richie sing before pursuing a successful 80s solo career?
   a) The Manhattans
   b) Chairmen of the Board
   c) The Commodores

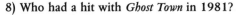

NOVICE

8) Who had a hit with *Ghost Town* in 1981?
   a) The Specials
   b) Dexy's Midnight Runners
   c) Madness

9) *Appetite for Destruction* was the 1987 debut album of which band?
   a) The Stone Roses
   b) Guns n' Roses
   c) The Beastie Boys

10) Which country provided the title for a 1981 hit by Kim Wilde?
   a) China
   b) Vietnam
   c) Cambodia

Answers: 1c, 2b, 3c, 4b, 5a, 6b, 7c, 8a, 9b, 10c

FASHION

1) Which British fashion designer said: 'I'm not that interested in fashion... When someone says that lime-green is the new black for this season, you just want to tell them to get a life.'?
   a) Vivienne Westwood
   b) Stella McCartney
   c) Bruce Oldfield

NOVICE

2) Which world-famous designer originally had the surname Lifshitz?
   a) Calvin Klein
   b) Ralph Lauren
   c) Charles Frederick Worth

3) Whose fashion house was founded in 1947 at 30 Avenue Montaigne, Paris?
   a) Pierre Balmain
   b) Yves St. Laurent
   c) Christian Dior

4) Who was appointed chief designer at the French couture house Chloe in March 1997?
   a) Stella McCartney
   b) Ossie Clark
   c) Vivienne Westwood

5) The Irishman Philip Treacy is renowned for his designs of what?
   a) Hats
   b) Shoes
   c) Handbags

6) Which French fashion designer said: 'There is time for work. And time for love. That leaves no other time.'?
   a) Jean-Paul Gaultier
   b) Coco Chanel
   c) Pierre Cardin

7) In what year was Louis Vuitton's first shop founded at 2 rue de Pont-Neuf in Paris?
   a) 1954
   b) 1854
   c) 1754

8) Which couturier was Peace Ambassador to UNESCO in 1991?
   a) Pierre Cardin
   b) Yves St. Laurent
   c) Coco Chanel

9) Which supermodel starred with Hugh Grant in the film *Sirens*?
   a) Naomi Campbell
   b) Kate Moss
   c) Elle MacPherson

10) Which celebrity became the brand ambassador for Givenchy?
    a) The Duchess of Windsor
    b) Twiggy
    c) Audrey Hepburn

NOVICE

Answers: 1c, 2b, 3c, 4a, 5a, 6b, 7b, 8a, 9c, 10c

GILBERT AND SULLIVAN

EXPERT

1) Which G&S opera is set in the Cornish village of Rederring?
   a) *The Pirates of Penzance*
   b) *HMS Pinafore*
   c) *Ruddigore*

2) Which G&S opera is based on a poem by Tennyson?
   a) *Iolanthe*
   b) *Princess Ida*
   c) *The Sorcerer*

3) In *The Yeoman of the Guard,* who instructs whom in the art of jesting?
   a) Jack Point instructs Wilfred Shadbolt
   b) Wilfred Shadbolt instructs Jack Point
   c) The Lieutenant of the Tower instructs Jack Point

4) Which of the G&S operas is subtitled, 'Bunthorne's Bride'?
   a) *Iolanthe*
   b) *Patience*
   c) *The Gondoliers*

5) Which of the G&S operas parodies the late Victorian cult of aestheticism?
   a) *Ruddigore*
   b) *Iolanthe*
   c) *Patience*

6) In which opera is the second Act set in the Palace Yard, Westminster, with Big Ben in the background?
   a) *The Yeoman of the Guard*
   b) *Iolanthe*
   c) *The Sorcerer*

7) Who informs the Court in *Trial by Jury* that 'To marry two at once is Burglaree!'?
   a) The Learned Judge
   b) The Usher
   c) The Counsel for the Plaintiff

8) Which G&S character has premises at 70 St. Mary Axe?
   a) John Wellington Wells in *The Sorcerer*
   b) Ernest Dummkopf in *The Grand Duke*
   c) Patience, the Dairymaid in *Patience*

9) Which G&S opera is set on a South Sea island?
   a) *The Pirates of Penzance*
   b) *Utopia Limited*
   c) *The Grand Duke*

10) Which G&S character is put into the unenviable position of having to try to cut off his own head?
   a) Ko-Ko in *The Mikado*
   b) Colonel Fairfax in *The Yeoman of the Guard*
   c) Robin Oakapple in *Ruddigore*

EXPERT

Answers: 1c, 2b, 3a, 4b, 5c, 6b, 7c, 8a, 9b, 10a

JAZZ

EXPERT

1) **With which instrument is Lester Young mainly associated?**
   a) Trumpet
   b) Piano
   c) Saxophone

2) **Whose most famous album was called *Kind of Blue*?**
   a) Charlie Parker
   b) Miles Davis
   c) Dizzy Gillespie

3) **What is the name of Wynton Marsalis's saxophone-playing brother?**
   a) Ellis
   b) Branford
   c) Miles

4) **Which jazz pianist was nicknamed 'Fatha'?**
   a) Earl Hines
   b) Oscar Peterson
   c) Duke Ellington

5) **Which legendary female vocalist began her career with the Chick Webb Orchestra?**
   a) Billie Holiday
   b) Ella Fitzgerald
   c) Sarah Vaughan

6) What was 'Dizzy' Gillespie's real first name?
   a) Edward
   b) Desmond
   c) John

7) Which big band had the song *One O'Clock Jump* as its signature tune?
   a) Count Basie Orchestra
   b) Cab Calloway Orchestra
   c) Duke Ellington Orchestra

8) Which saxophonist recorded *A Love Supreme* in 1964?
   a) Dexter Gordon
   b) John Coltrane
   c) Sonny Rollins

EXPERT

9) With which instrument is Charlie Mingus mainly associated?
   a) Trumpet
   b) Drums
   c) Bass

10) Which jazz guitarist played with Stephane Grappelli in the Quintet of the Hot Club of France in the 1930s?
   a) Joe Pass
   b) Charlie Christian
   c) Django Reinhardt

Answers: 1c, 2b, 3b, 4a, 5b, 6c, 7a, 8b, 9c, 10c

MUSIC AND ARTS 1

1) In which city is the Burrell Collection of art kept?
   a) Dublin
   b) Belfast
   c) Glasgow

2) Who wrote the lyrics to the Andrew Lloyd Webber musical *Starlight Express*?
   a) Tim Rice
   b) Richard Stilgoe
   c) Ben Elton

NOVICE

3) Which world leader wrote a play called *The Jeweller's Shop* which was adapted into a movie starring Burt Lancaster?
   a) Bill Clinton
   b) Vaclav Havel
   c) Pope John Paul II

4) Which 20th century artist painted *The Persistence of Memory*?
   a) Salvador Dali
   b) Pablo Picasso
   c) Henri Matisse

5) Who composed the patriotic US song *God Bless America*?
   a) George Gershwin
   b) Cole Porter
   c) Irving Berlin

6) For what type of drama did the Whitehall Theatre in London become famous?
   a) Shakespeare
   b) Farce
   c) Melodrama

7) Who founded the Bauhaus School of Art, Design and Architecture in 1919?
   a) Mies van der Rohe
   b) Walter Benjamin
   c) Walter Gropius

8) Who composed the operas *Jenufa* and *The Cunning Little Vixen*?
   a) Leoš Janáček
   b) Bedrich Smetana
   c) Alban Berg

9) Which illustrator created the girls' school St. Trinian's?
   a) Ronald Searle
   b) Gerald Scarfe
   c) Ralph Steadman

10) Under what name did George Galvin become a star of the music hall in the late 19th century?
   a) Dan Leno
   b) Little Tich
   c) George Robey

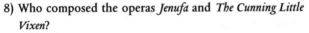

Answers: 1c, 2b, 3c, 4a, 5c, 6b, 7c, 8a, 9a, 10a

MUSIC AND ARTS 2

EXPERT

1) With which instrument is James Galway associated?
   a) Violin
   b) Flute
   c) Clarinet

2) How is the 19th century painting entitled *Arrangement in Black and Grey* better known?
   a) Whistler's Mother
   b) The Fighting Temeraire
   c) The Stag at Bay

3) Who played Yorick in the Kenneth Branagh film version of *Hamlet*?
   a) Tommy Cooper
   b) Ken Dodd
   c) Frankie Howerd

4) Which of the following familiar sights was designed by the British architect Sir Giles Gilbert Scott?
   a) The red telephone kiosk
   b) The Tube map
   c) The logo of the Olympic Games

5) To which institution are the royalties of J. M. Barrie's play *Peter Pan* paid?
   a) The Red Cross
   b) Great Ormond Street Hospital
   c) The Natural History Museum

6) What happened, after the sitter's death, to the 1954 portrait of Winston Churchill commissioned by parliament and painted by Graham Sutherland?
   a) It was sold to an American gallery
   b) It was destroyed by Churchill's wife
   c) It was stolen

7) Who described himself as having 'a talent to amuse'?
   a) Peter Ustinov
   b) Oscar Wilde
   c) Noel Coward

8) In which British city is there a statue of the cartoon character Desperate Dan?
   a) Cardiff
   b) Birmingham
   c) Dundee

9) Where in Spain was Pablo Picasso born?
   a) Malaga
   b) Barcelona
   c) Seville

10) Which architect designed the pyramids outside the Louvre in Paris?
   a) Frank Gehry
   b) I. M. Pei
   c) Renzo Piano

Answers: 1b, 2a, 3b, 4a, 5b, 6b, 7c, 8c, 9a, 10b

MUSIC AND ARTS 3

EXPERT

1) Henri Cartier-Bresson is best remembered for his work in which art form?
a) Dance
b) Architecture
c) Photography

2) Which special day is the birthday of the character Frederic the Pirate Apprentice in the Gilbert & Sullivan opera *The Pirates of Penzance*?
a) Christmas Day
b) February 29th
c) New Year's Day

3) In which US state is the Newport Jazz Festival held?
a) Pennsylvania
b) New Jersey
c) Rhode Island

4) In which of the performing arts did Merce Cunningham make his name?
a) Theatre
b) Music
c) Dance

5) Which 19th century British artist painted *The Boyhood of Raleigh*?
a) Sir John Everett Millais
b) Sir Edward Burne-Jones
c) Lord Leighton

6) Which famous comic book character was created by Frank Hampson?
   a) Dan Dare
   b) Batman
   c) Dennis the Menace

7) How was the actress Beatrice Stella Tanner better known?
   a) Ellen Terry
   b) Sarah Bernhardt
   c) Mrs Patrick Campbell

8) Who wrote the poem on which Benjamin Britten based his opera *Peter Grimes*?
   a) George Crabbe
   b) William Wordsworth
   c) John Keats

9) For what type of music is Ira D. Sankey best remembered?
   a) Music hall songs
   b) Hymns
   c) Brass band music

10) Where was the conductor Leopold Stokowski born?
    a) London
    b) Berlin
    c) Moscow

EXPERT

Answers: 1c, 2b, 3c, 4c, 5a, 6a, 7c, 8a, 9b, 10a

MUSICALS

EXPERT

1) Who wrote the lyrics for *West Side Story*?
   a) Stephen Sondheim
   b) Leonard Bernstein
   c) Oscar Hammerstein

2) Which author wrote the original story on which Andrew Lloyd Webber based *The Phantom of the Opera*?
   a) Guy de Maupassant
   b) Gaston Leroux
   c) Victor Hugo

3) Who wrote the musical *The Boy Friend*?
   a) Julian Slade
   b) Sandy Wilson
   c) Flanders and Swann

4) Which musical, which included lyrics by Tim Rice and music by Elton John, was released by Disney in 1994 and later became a spectacular stage show?
   a) *Aladdin*
   b) *Quasimodo*
   c) *The Lion King*

5) In which musical does the song *You'll Never Walk Alone*, later to become a football anthem, feature?
   a) *Carousel*
   b) *Oklahoma*
   c) *Showboat*

6) Who adapted G. B. Shaw's play *Pygmalion* to create the musical *My Fair Lady*?
   a) Rodgers and Hammerstein
   b) Lerner and Loewe
   c) Rodgers and Hart

7) Who wrote the 1960 musical *Oliver!*?
   a) Andrew Lloyd Webber
   b) Lionel Blair
   c) Lionel Bart

8) Which musical, first produced in the 1930s and revived in the 1980s, featured the song *The Lambeth Walk*?
   a) *Me and My Girl*
   b) *42nd Street*
   c) *Top Hat*

9) Which musical, first staged in 1968, was described as 'the American Tribal Love-Rock Musical'?
   a) *Follies*
   b) *Oh! Calcutta!*
   c) *Hair*

10) In which musical do the characters Velma Kelly, Roxie Hart and Billy Flynn appear?
   a) *Guys and Dolls*
   b *Chicago*
   c) *On the Town*

Answers: 1a, 2b, 3b, 4c, 5a, 6b, 7c, 8a, 9c, 10b

EXPERT

NINETIES MUSIC

1) **Which of the following was a member of Boyzone?**
   a) Stephen Gately
   b) Mark Owen
   c) Jason Orange

2) **Which artist released a 1999 album called *Midnite Vultures*?**
   a) Prince
   b) Beck
   c) Eminem

NOVICE

3) **From which English city do the band Blur come?**
   a) Winchester
   b) Colchester
   c) Salisbury

4) **Who had a No. 1 hit with *Everything Changes*?**
   a) Boyzone
   b) New Kids on the Block
   c) Take That

5) **In which year did Kurt Cobain commit suicide?**
   a) 1993
   b) 1994
   c) 1995

6) How old was Billie Piper when her debut single *Because We Want To* made it to No. 1?
   a) 14
   b) 15
   c) 16

7) Which group had a first UK No. 1 in 1995 with the song *Fairground*?
   a) Simply Red
   b) Suede
   c) Erasure

8) Who wrote the song *I Will Always Love You*, a hit for Whitney Houston in 1992?
   a) Dolly Parton
   b) Reba McIntire
   c) Emmylou Harris

9) With which group do you associate Neil Hannon?
   a) Travis
   b) Blur
   c) The Divine Comedy

10) Which artist recorded an album called *Graffiti Bridge* in 1990?
   a) Prince
   b) David Bowie
   c) Michael Jackson

NOVICE

Answers: 1a, 2b, 3b, 4c, 5b, 6b, 7a, 8a, 9c, 10a

OPERA 1

1) Which famous operatic soprano was nicknamed 'La Stupenda'?
   a) Joan Sutherland
   b) Maria Callas
   c) Kiri te Kanawa

2) Which British composer's operatic works include *Death in Venice* and *Peter Grimes*?
   a) Michael Tippett
   b) Benjamin Britten
   c) Arthur Sullivan

3) What nationality is Aida in Verdi's opera of that name?
   a) Egyptian
   b) Ethiopian
   c) Italian

4) What is the name of the bird catcher in Mozart's *The Magic Flute*?
   a) Sarastro
   b Monostatos
   c) Papageno

5) What is the name of Beethoven's only opera?
   a) *Fidelio*
   b) *Leonora*
   c) *Egmont*

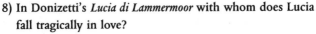

6) In which of Wagner's operas does the hero enter in a boat drawn by a swan?
   a) *Siegfried*
   b) *Tannhäuser*
   c) *Lohengrin*

7) Which of the following operas was written by Claude Debussy?
   a) *Pelléas and Mélisande*
   b) *L'Enfant et les Sortilèges*
   c) *The Pearl Fishers*

8) In Donizetti's *Lucia di Lammermoor* with whom does Lucia fall tragically in love?
   a) Rodolfo
   b) Edgardo
   c) Arturo

9) Which Italian composer wrote an opera set in the Californian Gold Rush?
   a) Verdi
   b) Donizetti
   c) Puccini

10) In which opera can you hear the aria *Vesti la Giubba*?
   a) *Pagliacci*
   b) *Rigoletto*
   c) *La Bohème*

Answers: 1a, 2b, 3b, 4c, 5a, 6c, 7a, 8b, 9c, 10a

OPERA 2

1) In Puccini's *La Bohème* Colline sings a touching aria of
   farewell to what?
   a) His paintbrushes
   b) His friends
   c) His coat

2) *Susanna's Secret* is an opera by Ermanno Wolf-Ferrari. What
   is her secret?
   a) She has a lover
   b) She has a child
   c) She is a cigarette smoker

GENIUS

3) Which musical work, set in the court of Queen Anne,
   includes the ballad *The Last Rose of Summer*?
   a) *Martha* by Friedrich von Flotow
   b) *A Village Romeo and Juliet* by Frederick Delius
   c) *Merrie England* by Edward German

4) In Verdi's *Rigoletto* what is the first name of the Duke of
   Mantua?
   a) Roberto
   b) Ricardo
   c) He isn't given one

5) What is the ultimate fate of the hero and heroine of
   Giordano's opera *Andrea Chenier*?
   a) They live happily ever after
   b) They are drowned in a shipwreck
   c) They are guillotined

6) Which of Verdi's operas tells the story of a 14th century doge of Genoa?
   a) *Don Carlos*
   b) *Simon Boccanegra*
   c) *I Due Foscari*

7) From which Russian opera are the well-known Polovtsian Dances taken?
   a) Borodin's *Prince Igor*
   b) Glinka's *Russlan and Ludmilla*
   c) Rimsky-Korsakov's *The Golden Cockerel*

GENIUS

8) In which Italian city is the famous La Fenice opera house?
   a) Venice
   b) Naples
   c) Rome

9) Which French composer wrote an opera based on Shakespeare's *Much Ado About Nothing*?
   a) Bizet
   b) Gounod
   c) Berlioz

10) Which of these operas deals with the rule of a Pharaoh of ancient Egypt and his wife Nefertiti?
   a) Verdi's *Aida*
   b) Glass's *Akhnaten*
   c) Mozart's *The Magic Flute*

Answers: 1c, 2c, 3a, 4c, 5c, 6b, 7a, 8a, 9c, 10b

SEVENTIES MUSIC

NOVICE

1) What was Blondie's first UK No. 1?
   a) *The Tide Is High*
   b) *Heart of Glass*
   c) *Hanging on the Telephone*

2) *Love Me for a Reason* was a hit for Boyzone in the 1990s. Who had a hit with the same song in the 1970s?
   a) The Osmonds
   b) The Jackson Five
   c) The Four Tops

3) Which group had a picture of Jerry Hall as a mermaid on the cover of one of their albums?
   a) Roxy Music
   b) Rolling Stones
   c) The Who

4) What was Terry Jacks's only UK No. 1?
   a) *Yellow River*
   b) *Spirit in the Sky*
   c) *Seasons in the Sun*

5) Which of the following was a member of The Sex Pistols?
   a) Glenn Matlock
   b) Mick Jones
   c) Rat Scabies

6) With whom did David Bowie collaborate on the 1977 album *Low*?
   a) Mick Jagger
   b) Brian Eno
   c) Tina Turner

7) Who had a hit in 1979 with *Up the Junction*?
   a) Selector
   b) Sweet Sensation
   c) Squeeze

8) In which year did The Who's drummer Keith Moon die?
   a) 1976
   b) 1977
   c) 1978

9) Which group had a 1973 hit with *Blockbuster*?
   a) Slade
   b) Sweet
   c) The Glitter Band

10) Errol Brown was the lead singer in which chart-topping 1970s group?
    a) Hot Chocolate
    b) Boney M
    c) Dawn

NOVICE

Answers: 1b, 2a, 3a, 4c, 5a, 6b, 7c, 8c, 9b, 10a

SIXTIES MUSIC

NOVICE

1) Who had a hit in 1964 with *House of the Rising Sun*?
   a) The Rolling Stones
   b) The Animals
   c) Manfred Mann

2) Jimi Hendrix recorded *All Along the Watchtower* in 1968 but who wrote it?
   a) Bob Dylan
   b) Eric Clapton
   c) Lennon and McCartney

3) To where did The Monkees take the last train in a 1966 hit song?
   a) Memphis
   b San Fernando
   c) Clarksville

4) In which year did The Beatles's *Sergeant Pepper's Lonely Hearts Club Band* album appear?
   a) 1967
   b) 1968
   c) 1969

5) Who wrote the song *Puppy Love*?
   a) Jerry Leiber and Mike Stoller
   b) Paul Anka
   c) Carole King

6) Who had a hit in 1964 with *Do Wah Diddy Diddy*?
   a) Herman's Hermits
   b) Manfred Mann
   c) Dave Dee, Dozy, Beaky, Mick and Tich

7) Which group was originally called Carl and the Passions?
   a) The Beach Boys
   b) The Kinks
   c) The Loving Spoonful

8) How was James Marcus Smith better known in the 1960s?
   a) Billy J. Kramer
   b) Billy Fury
   c) P. J. Proby

9) Which group released an album called *The Piper at the Gates of Dawn* in August 1967?
   a) Pink Floyd
   b) Procul Harum
   c) The Small Faces

10) Which sixties popstar died at a house once owned by A. A. Milne, the creator of Winnie the Pooh?
   a) Jimi Hendrix
   b) Janis Joplin
   c) Brian Jones

NOVICE

Answers: 1b, 2a, 3c, 4a, 5b, 6b, 7a, 8c, 9a, 10c

THEATRE 1

1) Whose play *The Mousetrap* holds the record for the longest-running stage production?
   a) Terence Rattigan
   b) Noel Coward
   c) Agatha Christie

2) Which former slave became a writer of comedies for the Roman stage?
   a) Plautus
   b) Terence
   c) Horace

3) Which comedy trio performs a stage version of all Shakespeare's plays in 90 minutes?
   a) The National Theatre of Brent
   b) Fascinating Aida
   c) The Reduced Shakespeare Company

4) At which London theatre was John Osborne's groundbreaking play *Look Back in Anger* first performed?
   a) Old Vic
   b) Windmill
   c) Royal Court

5) In the theatre what is a 'scrim'?
   a) A 'see through' curtain
   b) A make-up artist
   c) An area of the stage

NOVICE

6) Which of the following is a play by Chekhov?
   a) *The Wild Duck*
   b) *The Birds*
   c) *The Seagull*

7) Which of the following is not one of the three theatres at the National Theatre?
   a) Cottesloe
   b) Gielgud
   c) Lyttelton

8) How many plays are thought to have been written by the Spanish renaissance dramatist Lope de Vega?
   a) 37
   b) 256
   c) More than 2,000

9) Who was the first actor to be knighted?
   a) Laurence Olivier
   b) Henry Irving
   c) Herbert Beerbohm Tree

10) Which British playwright is commonly associated with the Hull Truck Theatre?
   a) Alan Ayckbourn
   b) Caryl Churchill
   c) John Godber

NOVICE

Answers: 1c, 2b, 3c, 4c, 5a, 6c, 7b, 8c, 9b, 10c

THEATRE 2

1) Who wrote the plays *The Homecoming* and *The Birthday Party*?
   a) Alan Bennett
   b) Tom Stoppard
   c) Harold Pinter

2) In which town is there a theatre named after the famous stage designer Edward Gordon Craig?
   a) Slough
   b) Stevenage
   c) Milton Keynes

3) An actress using which word shocked some of the audience at the first performance of George Bernard Shaw's play *Pygmalion* in 1914?
   a) Bloody
   b) Bugger
   c) Bastard

4) Which playwright became Charlie Chaplin's father-in-law in 1943?
   a) J. M. Barrie
   b) Clifford Odets
   c) Eugene O'Neill

5) The poet Coleridge described watching which actor as 'like reading Shakespeare by flashes of lightning'?
   a) David Garrick
   b) Edmund Kean
   c) William Macready

EXPERT

6) In which century did women first appear on a public stage in England?
   a) 16th
   b) 17th
   c) 18th

7) Which musical was based on stories by Christopher Isherwood?
   a) *Cabaret*
   b) *Hello Dolly*
   c) *The Little Shop of Horrors*

EXPERT

8) In 1995 who walked out of the West End production of Simon Gray's play *Cell Mates*, suffering from stress, and went missing for several days?
   a) Stephen Fry
   b) Rik Mayall
   c) Rowan Atkinson

9) Who wrote the controversial 1995 play *Blasted*?
   a) Edward Bond
   b) Sarah Kane
   c) David Mamet

10) Which musician and singer appeared as a boy in a West End production of *Oliver!*, playing the Artful Dodger?
   a) David Bowie
   b) Sting
   c) Phil Collins

Answers: 1c, 2b, 3a, 4c, 5b, 6b, 7a, 8a, 9b, 10c

THE
NATURAL
WORLD

ANIMALS 1

1) Which of the following is an alternative name for the scaly anteater?
   a) Armadillo
   b) Wapiti
   c) Pangolin

2) What type of creature is a sidewinder?
   a) Beetle
   b) Snake
   c) Bird

NOVICE

3) Which creature derives its name from the Spanish word for lizard?
   a) Crocodile
   b) Cayman
   c) Alligator

4) How many hearts does an earthworm have?
   a) 1
   b) 3
   c) 10

5) What are young eels called?
   a) Elvers
   b) Elmets
   c) Eldreds

6) What is the collective noun for a group of leopards?
   a) A skulk
   b) A leap
   c) A pounce

7) To which of the following animals is the rock hyrax or rock rabbit most closely related?
   a) Tiger
   b) Kangaroo
   c) Elephant

8) On which continent did the extinct carnivore called the thylacine live?
   a) Asia
   b) Australia
   c) Africa

NOVICE

9) What type of animal is a bongo?
   a) Fish
   b) Monkey
   c) Antelope

10) How many legs does a crab have?
   a) 8
   b) 10
   c) 12

Answers: 1c, 2b, 3c, 4c, 5a, 6b, 7c, 8b, 9c, 10b

ANIMALS 2

1) What is the largest rodent in the world?
   a) Agouti
   b) Capybara
   c) Coypu

2) What type of animal is a kudu?
   a) Antelope
   b) Deer
   c) Reptile

EXPERT

3) Which animal, a member of the giraffe family, was first discovered in the African rainforests in 1901?
   a) Quagga
   b) Okapi
   c) Wapiti

4) What kind of creature is a pipistrelle?
   a) Bird
   b) Bat
   c) Beetle

5) Which of the following animals is a monotreme?
   a) Platypus
   b) Opossum
   c) Wallaby

6) In which of the following continents are bears not found?
   a) Africa
   b) Europe
   c) Australia

7) What are the young of hedgehogs called?
   a) Hoglets
   b) Hedgelets
   c) Hedgelings

8) How long does an elephant's pregnancy normally last?
   a) 12 months
   b) 22 months
   c) 26 months

EXPERT

9) What is another name for the pygmy chimpanzee?
   a) Aye-Aye
   b) Colobus
   c) Bonobo

10) How many horns does a white rhino have?
   a) 1
   b) 2
   c) 3

Answers: 1b, 2a, 3b, 4b, 5a, 6c, 7a, 8b, 9c, 10b

ANIMALS OF BRITAIN 1

1) **What type of creature is a slow worm?**
   a) A worm
   b) A snake
   c) A lizard

2) **Which mammal was first introduced to Britain by Lord Rothschild in 1902?**
   a) The edible dormouse
   b) The mink
   c) The harvest mouse

EXPERT

3) **Which common British mammal has the scientific name *Talpa europaea*?**
   a) The badger
   b) The mole
   c) The hedgehog

4) **Which animal lives in a 'holt'?**
   a) A badger
   b) A fox
   c) An otter

5) **Which is the smallest British mammal?**
   a) The yellow-necked mouse
   b) The pygmy shrew
   c) The common dormouse

6) Which British deer is distinguishable by a spotted coat and broad-bladed antlers?
   a) The fallow deer
   b) The red deer
   c) The roe deer

7) What are the young of the pine marten called?
   a) Cubs
   b) Kits
   c) Pups

8) How many species of bat are there in the British Isles?
   a) 5
   b) 12
   c) 16

EXPERT

9) What are 'spraints'?
   a) The droppings of an otter
   b) The tracks of a badger
   c) The feet of a fox

10) Which common mammal was introduced to Britain in the 12th century as a valuable source of meat and skins?
   a) The otter
   b) The goat
   c) The rabbit

Answers: 1c, 2a, 3b, 4c, 5b, 6a, 7b, 8c, 9a, 10c

ANIMALS OF BRITAIN 2

1) How many species of snake are native to the British Isles?
   a) Four
   b) Three
   c) Two

2) Which animal lives in a 'form'?
   a) Hare
   b) Squirrel
   c) Rabbit

3) Which of the following is a British butterfly?
   a) Camberwell Beauty
   b) Peckham Painted Lady
   c) Greenwich Admiral

4) What is the name given to a male badger?
   a) Buck
   b) Boar
   c) Dog

5) Which creature has species called Bechstein's and Daubenton's?
   a) Butterfly
   b) Bee
   c) Bat

EXPERT

6) Which British island is claimed to have the largest colony of North Atlantic gannets in the world?
   a) Lindisfarne
   b) Lundy
   c) St. Kilda

7) What is the better known name of *Sciurus vulgaris*?
   a) Water vole
   b) Common shrew
   c) Red squirrel

8) The last book Charles Darwin published in his life was about which creature widely found in Britain?
   a) Earthworm
   b) Slug
   c) Snail

9) Which of the following animals hibernates?
   a) Mole
   b) Hedgehog
   c) Rabbit

10) Which British bird is sometimes known as a yaffle?
   a) Treecreeper
   b) Green woodpecker
   c) Nuthatch

Answers: 1b, 2a, 3a, 4b, 5c, 6c, 7c, 8a, 9b, 10b

BIRDS OF THE WORLD 1

1) What type of birds did Charles Darwin study on the Galapagos Islands which helped to develop his ideas on natural selection?
   a) Seabirds
   b) Finches
   c) Storks

2) What is the name of the world's smallest bird?
   a) Mosquito hummingbird
   b) Pygmy hummingbird
   c) Bee hummingbird

3) To which family of birds does the kookaburra belong?
   a) Kingfisher
   b) Parrot
   c) Heron

4) Which of the following is the only bird that hunts by sense of smell?
   a) Lyre bird
   b) Kiwi
   c) Emu

5) In which continent would you find budgerigars in their natural habitat?
   a) Australia
   b) Asia
   c) South America

NOVICE

6) Which bird has varieties called Fairy, Black-footed and Crested?
   a) Gull
   b) Goose
   c) Penguin

7) What makes a hummingbird hum?
   a) The movement of its legs
   b) The movement of its beak
   c) The movement of its wings

8) What is the state bird of Florida?
   a) Pelican
   b) Mockingbird
   c) Roadrunner

9) What is the more common name for *Erithacus rubecula*?
   a) Robin
   b) Cuckoo
   c) Hoopoe

10) On which island was the last dodo seen in the 17th century?
   a) Mauritius
   b) Madagascar
   c) New Guinea

NOVICE

Answers: 1b, 2c, 3a, 4b, 5a, 6c, 7c, 8b, 9a, 10a

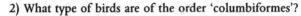

BIRDS OF THE WORLD 2

1) Which species of penguin has a crest of feathers on its head?
   a) Emperor penguin
   b) Gentoo penguin
   c) Rockhopper penguin

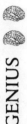

2) What type of birds are of the order 'columbiformes'?
   a) Hawks
   b) Doves and pigeons
   c) Finches

3) Which of the following is the largest eagle in the Americas?
   a) Harpy eagle
   b) Bald eagle
   c) Mountain eagle

4) Which of the following is the name of an American diving bird?
   a) The Blue-Footed Booby
   b) The Blue-Footed Loon
   c) The Blue-Footed Dolt

5) What sound does a flamingo make?
   a) It honks like a goose
   b) It makes no sound
   c) It has a clear, piercing scream like a peacock's

6) Which of the following birds is now extinct?
   a) Black-capped chickadee
   b) Passenger pigeon
   c) Mountain bluebird

7) Which of the following is a bird?
   a) Lory
   b) Kudu
   c) Remora

8) To which family of birds does the quail belong?
   a) Coot
   b) Partridge
   c) Bustard

GENIUS

9) Which of the following is *not* the name of a species of owl?
   a) Chinese Spectacled owl
   b) Australian Masked owl
   c) Guatemalan Screech owl

10) The ostrich is the world's largest bird. What is the second largest?
   a) Emu
   b) Emperor penguin
   c) Albatross

Answers: 1c, 2b, 3a, 4a, 5a, 6b, 7a, 8b, 9a, 10a

BRITISH BIRDS

1) Which of the following birds is also known as the hedge sparrow?
   a) Dunnock
   b) Dotterel
   c) Dunlin

EXPERT

2) Which of these game birds has plumage that turns white in winter?
   a) Quail
   b) Capercaillie
   c) Ptarmigan

3) What is the smallest British bird?
   a) Wren
   b) Goldcrest
   c) Bluethroat

4) Which British bird has the scientific name of *Pica pica*?
   a) Magpie
   b) Jackdaw
   c) Carrion crow

5) What is the collective name for a group of owls?
   a) A house
   b) An assembly
   c) A parliament

6) Which British bird is the symbol of The Royal Society for the Protection of Birds?
   a) Avocet
   b) Robin
   c) Wren

7) Which of the following is another name for a song-thrush?
   a) Myrtle
   b) Marne
   c) Mavis

EXPERT

8) What type of bird is a greylag?
   a) Gull
   b) Goose
   c) Gannet

9) Which of the following is a British bird?
   a) Blue wagtail
   b) Red wagtail
   c) Yellow wagtail

10) Which bird was once known as the red-legged crow?
   a) Jay
   b) Chough
   c) Jackdaw

Answers: 1a, 2b, 3b, 4a, 5c, 6a, 7c, 8b, 9c, 10b

CATS AND DOGS

EXPERT

1) In greyhound racing in Britain, what colour jacket is worn by the dog in trap one?
   a) Yellow
   b) Blue
   c) Red

2) What is the name for a female cat which is breeding?
   a) Doe
   b) Queen
   c) Empress

3) Which of these characteristics is typical of a Siamese cat?
   a) Long hair
   b) Loud meow
   c) Striped coat

4) Which domestic dog breed is the heaviest?
   a) Saint Bernard
   b) Irish Wolfhound
   c) English Setter

5) From which country do Samoyed dogs originally come?
   a) China
   b) Russia
   c) Japan

6) Which Egyptian goddess is often depicted in the shape of a cat?
   a) Isis
   b) Hathor
   c) Bast

7) Which breed of dog has won Crufts' Best in Show prize most often?
   a) Cocker Spaniel
   b) Afghan Hound
   c) Miniature Poodle

EXPERT

8) Which small town in Northumberland gives its name to a type of terrier?
   a) Bedlington
   b) Tweedmouth
   c) Rothbury

9) In cartoons which cat was the sworn enemy of a bird called Tweety Pie?
   a) Topcat
   b) Sylvester
   c) Garfield

10) How many toes do cats have?
   a) Five toes on the forefeet and four on the hind feet
   b) Four toes on each foot
   c) Four toes on the forefeet and five on the hind feet

Answers: 1c, 2b, 3b, 4a, 5b, 6c, 7a, 8a, 9b, 10a

FARM ANIMALS

1) What type of animal is a Wessex Saddleback?
   a) Sheep
   b) Goat
   c) Pig

2) What is a female donkey called?
   a) Jenny
   b) Jilly
   c) Molly

GENIUS

3) Which animal is attacked by the disease 'vives'?
   a) Sheep
   b) Cow
   c) Horse

4) Which breed of cattle is also known as a Holstein?
   a) Jersey
   b) Friesian
   c) Aberdeen Angus

5) Which of the following is a name for a young female pig?
   a) Milt
   b) Silt
   c) Gilt

6) To which farmyard animal does the word 'caprine' refer?
   a) Goat
   b) Sheep
   c) Cow

7) Which of the following cheeses is made from sheep's milk?
   a) Gorgonzola
   b) Roquefort
   c) Edam

8) Which of the following words is a collective noun for a group of turkeys?
   a) Tile
   b) Beam
   c) Rafter

GENIUS

9) Which of the following is not a breed of pig?
   a) Berkshire
   b) Yorkshire
   c) Shropshire

10) What creature has breeds called Buff Orpington and Red Dorking?
   a) Pheasant
   b) Turkey
   c) Chicken

Answers: 1c, 2a, 3c, 4b, 5c, 6a, 7b, 8c, 9c, 10c

FICTIONAL ANIMALS

What were the following animals?

NOVICE

1) **Nana**
   a) The wolf that is Mowgli's foster-mother in *The Jungle Book*
   b) The dog in *The Incredible Journey*
   c) The Darling family dog in *Peter Pan*

2) **Cap'n Flint**
   a) Long John Silver's parrot in *Treasure Island*
   b) The parrot in the Doctor Dolittle books
   c) The parrot in Disney's film of *Aladdin*

3) **King Louie**
   a) The ape king in the Disney film of *The Jungle Book*
   b) The orang-utan in the Clint Eastwood film *Every Which Way But Loose*
   c) The ape in C. S. Lewis's *The Last Battle*

4) **Shardik**
   a) The dog in Jack London's *The Call of the Wild*
   b) A bear in a book of the same name by Richard Adams
   c) Aragorn's horse in *The Lord of the Rings*

5) **Aslan**
   a) The lion in C. S. Lewis's Narnia books
   b) One of the pigs in George Orwell's *Animal Farm*
   c) One of Black Beauty's stable companions

6) Great A'Tuin

   a) Cohen the Barbarian's horse in Terry Pratchett's Discworld novels

   b) The Crocodile God in the Discworld

   c) The World Turtle that carries the elephants that carry the Discworld

7) Shadowfax

   a) Gandalf's horse in *The Lord of the Rings*

   b) The armoured bear in Philip Pullman's *His Dark Materials* trilogy

   c) The chief wolf in C. S. Lewis's *The Lion, the Witch and the Wardrobe*

NOVICE

8) Hedwig

   a) The white goat in *Heidi*

   b) A rabbit in *Watership Down*

   c) Harry Potter's owl in J. K. Rowling's *Harry Potter* books

9) Rikki-Tikki-Tavi

   a) The snake in the Sherlock Holmes story *The Speckled Band*

   b) A mongoose in a story by Rudyard Kipling

   c) Hiawatha's hunting dog in Henry Longfellow's poem

10) Montmorency

   a) The leader of the stoats and weasels in *The Wind in the Willows*

   b) The dog in Jerome K. Jerome's *Three Men in a Boat*

   c) The caterpillar in *Alice in Wonderland*

Answers: 1c, 2a, 3a, 4b, 5a, 6c, 7a, 8c, 9b, 10b

HORSES AND PONIES

1) From which country do Eriskay ponies originate?
   a) Ireland
   b) Scotland
   c) Wales

2) On a horse where would you find the 'frog'?
   a) On its leg
   b) On its face
   c) On its hoof

3) Horses are usually measured in hands. How many inches in a hand?
   a) 3
   b) 4
   c) 5

4) Which of the following breeds of pony is now extinct?
   a) Galloway
   b) Exmoor
   c) Fjord

5) Which of the following is one of the three foundation sires of the Thoroughbred breed?
   a) Buckley Turk
   b) Manderley Arabian
   c) Byerley Turk

GENIUS

6) Which of the following is not a breed of horse?
   a) Percheron
   b) Bulgarian White
   c) Suffolk Punch

7) How many pairs of ribs do most horses have?
   a) 14
   b) 16
   c) 18

8) Which of the following was a prehistoric ancestor of the modern horse?
   a) Eohippus
   b) Plesiohippus
   c) Saurohippus

GENIUS

9) Which of the following is a breed as well as a colour variation?
   a) Skewbald
   b) Piebald
   c) Palomino

10) What is the name of the only breed of pony usually considered native to Ireland?
   a) Connemara
   b) Tipperary
   c) Waterford

Answers: 1b, 2c, 3b, 4a, 5c, 6b, 7c, 8a, 9c, 10a

INSECTS 1

NOVICE

1) The bite of which insect causes the disease known as sleeping sickness?
   a) Tsetse fly
   b) Mosquito
   c) Fruit fly

2) How many legs are there on each segment of a centipede?
   a) Two
   b) Four
   c) Six

3) What is the less colloquial name for the daddy-long-legs?
   a) Mayfly
   b) Cranefly
   c) Horsefly

4) What type of insects make up the order *Lepidoptera*?
   a) Bees and wasps
   b) Grasshoppers and crickets
   c) Butterflies and moths

5) Which of the following is *not* a name for a type of beetle?
   a) Stag beetle
   b) Stallion beetle
   c) Horse beetle

6) How is *Apis mellifera* better known?
   a) Tarantula
   b) Stag beetle
   c) Honey-bee

7) What is the name of the world's smallest butterfly?
   a) Lesser Batwing
   b) Tiny Hairstreak
   c) Western Pygmy Blue

8) Which of the following is a type of spider?
   a) Holas spider
   b) Bolas spider
   c) Molas spider

9) What is the name of the substance which makes up the exoskeletons of insects?
   a) Chitin
   b) Keratin
   c) Riboflavin

10) What are 'elytra'?
   a) Midges
   b) Wing covers
   c) Antennae

NOVICE

Answers: 1a, 2a, 3b, 4c, 5b, 6c, 7c, 8b, 9a, 10b

INSECTS 2

EXPERT

1) What is the average life-span of a queen honey-bee?
   a) Six months
   b) One year
   c) Two years

2) What colour are the spots on a common ladybird?
   a) Red
   b) Yellow
   c) Black

3) What are the fastest speeds at which some species of dragonfly can fly?
   a) 5 mph
   b) 10 mph
   c) 25 mph

4) Which of the following insects are part of the order *Hymenoptera*?
   a) Wasps
   b) Dragonflies
   c) Crickets

5) Where are the organs of hearing on a locust?
   a) Legs
   b) Abdomen
   c) Antennae

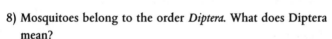

6) The world's largest spider is named after which biblical character?
   a) Samson
   b) Goliath
   c) Solomon

7) How many eyes does a bee have?
   a) Five
   b) Four
   c) Three

8) Mosquitoes belong to the order *Diptera*. What does Diptera mean?
   a) Two stomachs
   b) Two hearts
   c) Two wings

EXPERT

9) What type of creature is a 'hairstreak'?
   a) Beetle
   b) Ant
   c) Butterfly

10) What are an insect's malpighian tubes?
   a) Part of the excretory system
   b) Part of the insect's eye
   c) A type of antenna

Answers: 1c, 2c, 3c, 4a, 5b, 6b, 7a, 8c, 9c, 10a

NATURAL HISTORY 1

EXPERT

1) What is another name for the snow leopard?
   a) Ocelot
   b) Ounce
   c) Okapi

2) A koala bear eats the leaves from which tree?
   a) Foxtail palm
   b) Paperbark tree
   c) Eucalyptus tree

3) What type of animal is a 'gurnard'?
   a) Bird
   b) Snake
   c) Fish

4) Of what is oology the study?
   a) Grasses
   b) Birds' eggs
   c) Moths

5) What is the collective noun for a group of toads?
   a) A knot
   b) A blot
   c) A squat

6) What type of animal is a 'sooty mangabey'?
   a) A parrot
   b) A tropical fish
   c) A monkey

7) To which family of fish does the pilchard belong?
   a) Herring
   b) Wrasse
   c) Dogfish

8) What type of animal is a taipan?
   a) Rodent
   b) Snake
   c) Tortoise

EXPERT

9) What is a female swan called?
   a) Pen
   b) Cob
   c) Hen

10) Which of the following birds would be described as a 'ratite'?
   a) Eagle
   b) Condor
   c) Ostrich

Answers: 1b, 2c, 3c, 4b, 5a, 6c, 7a, 8b, 9a, 10c

NATURAL HISTORY 2

EXPERT

1) What does a pteridologist study?
   a) Prehistoric fish
   b) Ferns
   c) Beetles

2) What type of creature is a 'chuckwalla'?
   a) Bat
   b) Bird
   c) Lizard

3) What part of a toadstool is the 'pileus'?
   a) Cap
   b) Stalk
   c) Roots

4) What is the collective noun for a group of rhinoceroses?
   a) A crash
   b) A wallow
   c) A boast

5) To what family of plants does garlic belong?
   a) Rose
   b) Magnolia
   c) Lily

6) What colour is a giraffe's tongue?
   a) Blue
   b) Yellow
   c) Red

7) A seahorse is which of the following?
   a) Amphibian
   b) Mammal
   c) Fish

8) To which creatures does the word 'hirudinal' refer?
   a) Lizards
   b) Leeches
   c) Mites

EXPERT

9) What does an aphyllous plant lack?
   a) Leaves
   b) Flowers
   c) Buds

10) What is another name for Sibbald's Rorqual?
   a) Blue whale
   b) Bottle-nosed dolphin
   c) Great white shark

Answers: 1b, 2c, 3a, 4a, 5c, 6a, 7c, 8b, 9a, 10a

NATURAL HISTORY 3

1) **What is a common spadefoot?**
   a) A plant with broad spade-like leaves
   b) A type of toad
   c) A small wading bird

2) **What is the heaviest living land animal?**
   a) African elephant
   b) Indian elephant
   c) Rhinoceros

GENIUS

3) **Which seabirds are sometimes called 'Mother Carey's chickens'?**
   a) Stormy Petrels
   b) Albatrosses
   c) Puffins

4) **What do animals do when they estivate?**
   a) Give birth
   b) Digest their food
   c) Sleep in the summer

5) **What type of animal is a 'saki'?**
   a) Deer
   b) Bear
   c) Monkey

6) By what name is *Araucaria araucana* better known?
   a) The monkey puzzle tree
   b) The weeping willow
   c) The horse chestnut

7) How many toes do camels have on each foot?
   a) 2
   b) 3
   c) 4

8) What is a 'devil's coach-horse'?
   a) A beetle
   b) A mosquito
   c) A dragonfly

GENIUS

9) What does a dendrologist study?
   a) Trees
   b) Teeth
   c) Turtles

10) What is a gavial?
   a) A bird
   b) A reptile
   c) A mammal

Answers: 1b, 2a, 3a, 4c, 5c, 6a, 7a, 8a, 9a, 10b

PLANTS AND FLOWERS 1

EXPERT

1) **What is another name for the Christmas Rose?**
   a) Hyacinth
   b) Hellebore
   c) Hydrangea

2) **In which country did the tulip originate?**
   a) Turkey
   b) Holland
   c) Mexico

3) **To which of the following is the rose related?**
   a) Pumpkin
   b) Rhubarb
   c) Blackberry

4) **What is remarkable about the Asian plant called the Rafflesia?**
   a) Its roots stretch hundreds of yards underground
   b) It has the world's largest flower
   c) It only flowers once every five years

5) **Which flower is a symbol of imperial power in Japan?**
   a) Chrysanthemum
   b) Lily
   c) Rose

The Natural World

6) What type of plants does a mycologist study?
   a) Fungi
   b) Insect-eating plants
   c) Poisonous plants

7) By what name is the plant *Toxicodendron radicans* better known?
   a) Fly agaric
   b) Hemlock
   c) Poison ivy

8) What is a prickly pear?
   a) A fern
   b) A cactus
   c) A fruit

EXPERT

9) Which of the following plants was named after a 16th century Bavarian physician and botanist?
   a) Freesia
   b) Fuchsia
   c) Gardenia

10) From which plant is atropine derived?
   a) Foxglove
   b) Belladonna
   c) Henbane

Answers: 1b, 2a, 3c, 4b, 5a, 6a, 7c, 8b, 9b, 10b

PLANTS AND FLOWERS 2

1) Which of these flowers usually bloom for the shortest period of time?
   a) Roses
   b) Tulips
   c) Zinnias

2) What shape is a campanulate flower?
   a) Spear-shaped
   b) Shield-shaped
   c) Bell-shaped

EXPERT

3) In which of the following parts of a plant is the pollen found?
   a) Anther
   b) Calyx
   c) Sepal

4) What colour are the fruits of a deadly nightshade?
   a) Black
   b) Red
   c) White

5) Which of the following flowers is named after an 18th century French explorer?
   a) Begonia
   b) Bougainvillea
   c) Zinnia

6) What is the common name for the myosotis?
   a) Forget-me-not
   b) Bluebell
   c) Lilac

7) What part of the plant is the spice cinnamon made from?
   a) The bark
   b) The leaves
   c) The roots

8) What is a petiole?
   a) A leafstalk
   b) A root
   c) A small petal

EXPERT

9) Which flower is also called the Woodbine?
   a) Daisy
   b) Buttercup
   c) Honeysuckle

10) What colour is the flower edelweiss?
   a) Yellow
   b) White
   c) Red

Answers: 1b, 2c, 3a, 4a, 5b, 6a, 7a, 8a, 9c, 10b

REPTILES AND AMPHIBIANS

1) **What is a natterjack?**
   a) Toad
   b) Frog
   c) Lizard

2) **Which of the following is a member of the crocodile family?**
   a) Capybara
   b) Coatimundi
   c) Caiman

3) **Where is the only place in the world you can find the lizard-like reptile called the tuatara?**
   a) Mexico
   b) Japan
   c) New Zealand

4) **For what is an eft another name?**
   a) A toad
   b) A newt
   c) A tadpole

5) **Which of the following snakes is not poisonous?**
   a) Copperhead
   b) Water Moccasin
   c) Common garter snake

NOVICE

6) Which of the following is not a reptile?
   a) Smooth newt
   b) Adder
   c) Slow worm

7) What is the better known name for the British amphibian *Rana temporaria*?
   a) Common toad
   b) Great crested newt
   c) Common frog

8) Which of the following is a species of alligator?
   a) Vietnamese alligator
   b) Japanese alligator
   c) Chinese alligator

9) To which order of reptiles do snakes belong?
   a) *Crocodilia*
   b) *Squamata*
   c) *Testudinata*

10) What is the world's largest living turtle?
   a) Leatherback turtle
   b) Loggerhead sea turtle
   c) Green turtle

NOVICE

Answers: 1a, 2c, 3c, 4b, 5c, 6a, 7c, 8c, 9b, 10a

TREES

EXPERT

1) **To which family of trees does the sycamore belong?**
   a) Maple
   b) Elm
   c) Willow

2) **From which small tree do sloe berries come?**
   a) Hawthorn
   b) Whitethorn
   c) Blackthorn

3) **From what does the sequoia, the world's largest tree, take its name?**
   a) The Greek word for 'giant'
   b) A Cherokee Indian leader
   c) A giant in Native American mythology

4) **What does 'bonsai' mean literally?**
   a) House tree
   b) Planting in a tray
   c) Small tree

5) **Which of the following trees is particularly noted for the hardness of its wood?**
   a) Hornbeam
   b) Dogwood
   c) Hawthorn

6) Which of the following is not a genuine tree?
   a) Balsa
   b) Bamboo
   c) Bay

7) From which tree was the English longbow traditionally made?
   a) Yew
   b) Ash
   c) Birch

8) Which of the following is a deciduous rather than an evergreen tree?
   a) Scots pine
   b) Juniper
   c) Aspen

9) What is the common name for *Quercus robur*?
   a) Ash
   b) Oak
   c) Silver birch

10) Of which continent is the gingko tree a native?
   a) Europe
   b) Africa
   c) Asia

EXPERT

Answers: 1a, 2c, 3b, 4b, 5a, 6b, 7a, 8c, 9b, 10c

PEOPLE

BIRTHPLACES

Where were the following famous people born?

1) **Sir Alexander Fleming**
   a) New Zealand
   b) Scotland
   c) Canada

2) **Alfred Nobel**
   a) Switzerland
   b) Sweden
   c) Germany

3) **Shirley Bassey**
   a) Scotland
   b) England
   c) Wales

4) **Pierce Brosnan**
   a) Ireland
   b) France
   c) USA

5) **Emile Zola**
   a) Italy
   b) France
   c) Belgium

EXPERT

6) Carl Gustav Jung
   a) Switzerland
   b) Germany
   c) Austria

7) Nicole Kidman
   a) Hawaii
   b) Australia
   c) England

8) Nasser Hussain
   a) India
   b) Pakistan
   c) England

9) Claudia Schiffer
   a) Austria
   b) Germany
   c) USA

10) Keanu Reeves
   a) USA
   b) Israel
   c) Lebanon

EXPERT

Answers: 1b, 2b, 3c, 4a, 5b, 6a, 7a, 8a, 9b, 10c

CELEBRITIES 1

1) Whose real name is Gordon Sumner?
   a) Meatloaf
   b) Sting
   c) Bono

2) Who was the winner of the first series of *Big Brother* in 2000?
   a) Jade Goody
   b) Kate Lawler
   c) Craig Phillips

NOVICE

3) Carol Vorderman gained a degree at Cambridge in what subject?
   a) Maths
   b) Engineering
   c) English Literature

4) Whose stepfather was Hector Barrantes?
   a) Sarah Ferguson
   b) Paula Yates
   c) Princess Diana

5) In which US state was Jerry Hall born?
   a) California
   b) Alaska
   c) Texas

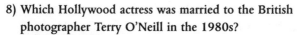

6) What is the family name of Princess Stephanie of Monaco?
   a) Grimaldi
   b) Visconti
   c) Medici

7) Kim Basinger and Alec Baldwin's daughter shares a name with which country?
   a) Ireland
   b) Colombia
   c) Zambia

8) Which Hollywood actress was married to the British photographer Terry O'Neill in the 1980s?
   a) Demi Moore
   b) Faye Dunaway
   c) Goldie Hawn

9) For what crime was Stephen Fry jailed when he was a teenager?
   a) Joyriding
   b) Credit card fraud
   c) Drugs possession

10) Where was nightclub owner Peter Stringfellow born?
   a) London
   b) Manchester
   c) Sheffield

NOVICE

Answers: 1b, 2c, 3b, 4a, 5c, 6a, 7a, 8b, 9b, 10c

CELEBRITIES 2

1) Who is the subject of the biography by Melvyn Bragg entitled *Rich*?
   a) Keith Richard
   b) Richard Burton
   c) Richard Branson

2) Which actor was Al Gore's room-mate at Harvard?
   a) Richard Dreyfuss
   b) Dustin Hoffman
   c) Tommy Lee Jones

NOVICE

3) Where was Bruce Willis born?
   a) West Germany
   b) England
   c) United States

4) As what is Nicky Clarke famous?
   a) Male model
   b) Hairdresser
   c) Dress designer

5) How old was River Phoenix when he died?
   a) 21
   b) 22
   c) 23

6) Which of the following singers was a gravedigger before he hit the big time?
   a) Julio Iglesias
   b) Barry Manilow
   c) Rod Stewart

7) Which celebrity's real name is Katie Price?
   a) Jordan
   b) Caprice
   c) Madonna

8) Which actor apparently ate a live cockroach in the film *Vampire's Kiss*?
   a) John Malkovich
   b) Nicholas Cage
   c) Keanu Reeves

9) Which film star is reported to have said 'Some people collect art, I collect husbands'?
   a) Elizabeth Taylor
   b) Zsa Zsa Gabor
   c) Joan Collins

10) Where was Terry Wogan born?
   a) Dublin
   b) Limerick
   c) Ballynahinch

NOVICE

Answers: 1b, 2c, 3a, 4b, 5c, 6c, 7a, 8b, 9a, 10b

CELEBRITIES 3

1) Where in the UK is there a theatre named after Bob Hope?
   a) Ealing
   b) Elstree
   c) Eltham

2) What links singer Cliff Richard and actress Vivien Leigh?
   a) They were cousins
   b) They lived (at different times) at the same address
   c) They were both born in India

EXPERT

3) Whose first recording experience was singing 'R2-D2, we wish you a Merry Christmas' for a *Star Wars* album entitled *Christmas in the Stars*?
   a) Noel Gallagher
   b) Jon Bon Jovi
   c) Ricky Martin

4) Which celebrity won the first series of the UK *I'm a Celebrity! Get me out of here!*?
   a) Tony Blackburn
   b) Tara Palmer-Tomkinson
   c) Kerry McFadden

5) Which actor always wore a toupee when playing James Bond?
   a) Timothy Dalton
   b) Sean Connery
   c) Roger Moore

6) What is the first name of the Saatchi brother married to celebrity chef Nigella Lawson?
   a) Charles
   b) Maurice
   c) Kevin

7) Which member of the Monty Python team was born in Weston-super-Mare?
   a) John Cleese
   b) Eric Idle
   c) Terry Jones

8) When was Pop Idol judge Simon Cowell born?
   a) 1949
   b) 1959
   c) 1969

9) Which American chat show host said of himself, 'If it weren't for the coffee, I'd have no personality whatsoever'?
   a) Johnny Carson
   b) David Letterman
   c) Jay Leno

10) Where was supermodel Naomi Campbell born?
   a) Streatham, south London
   b) Brooklyn, New York
   c) Handsworth, Birmingham

Answers: 1c, 2c, 3b, 4a, 5b, 6a, 7a, 8b, 9b, 10a

EPONYMS

Identify the people who gave their names to these words.
Nationalities and years of birth and death are shown to
provide a clue.

EXPERT

1) Shrapnel
   a) A major-general in the British Army (1761–1842)
   b) A Swedish scientist (1880–1947)
   c) A German arms manufacturer (1872–1940)

2) Bowdlerise
   a) A Scottish educationalist (1800–1888)
   b) An English doctor of medicine (1754–1825)
   c) An English vicar and writer (1789–1756)

3) Spoonerism
   a) A professor of English at Cambridge (1832–1865)
   b) An Irish newspaper editor (1870–1934)
   c) An English churchman and Oxford don (1844–1930)

4) Leotard
   a) A French acrobat (1842–1870)
   b) An English ballet dancer (1900–1968)
   c) A Dutch long-distance runner (1899–1971)

5) Sandwich
   a) A French gourmet and writer (1798–1862)
   b) An English aristocrat and politician (1718–1792)
   c) A Belgian restaurateur (1870–1942)

6) Sousaphone

a) An American composer and bandleader (1854–1932)

b) An Italian maker of musical instruments (1842–1882)

c) An English Master of the King's Music (1891–1952)

7) Bloomers

a) An English novelist (1831–1901)

b) An American feminist (1818–1894)

c) A French couturier (1900–1983)

8) Boycott

a) An Irish land agent (1832–1897)

b) An American store-keeper (1810–1882)

c) An English social reformer (1832–1905)

EXPERT

9) Cardigan

a) A Scottish writer and politician (1799–1873)

b) The wife of a Scottish clergyman (1800–1848)

c) A British cavalry officer (1797–1868)

10) Saxophone

a) An American bandleader and performer (1821–1889)

b) A Belgian musical instrument designer (1814–1894)

c) A German industrialist and amateur musician (1864–1913)

Answers: 1a, 2b, 3c, 4a, 5b, 6a, 7b, 8a, 9c, 10b

EXPLORERS

1) What nationality was Christopher Columbus?
   a) Spanish
   b) Portuguese
   c) Italian

2) Which explorer was the first European to sail around the southern tip of Africa?
   a) Bartolomeu Dias
   b) Ferdinand Magellan
   c) Vasco da Gama

3) What was the name of the ship in which Sir Francis Drake circumnavigated the world in 1577–1580?
   a) *The Mary Rose*
   b) *The Discovery*
   c) *The Golden Hind*

4) Which polar explorer was the first to pinpoint the location of the North Magnetic Pole in 1831?
   a) Sir John Franklin
   b) Sir James Ross
   c) Sir Edward Parry

5) Which continent were Robert O'Hara Burke and William John Wills attempting to cross from south to north and back when they died in 1861?
   a) Australia
   b) Antarctica
   c) Africa

EXPERT

6) Which 19th century British explorer not only made dangerous journeys in Africa but also translated the Kama Sutra?
   a) David Livingstone
   b) Mungo Park
   c) Sir Richard Burton

7) Which two Canadian cities were founded by the 17th century French explorer Samuel de Champlain?
   a) Quebec and Toronto
   b) Quebec and Ottawa
   c) Quebec and Montreal

EXPERT

8) Where did Captain Cook meet his death in 1778?
   a) Hawaii
   b) Australia
   c) Tahiti

9) Francisco de Orellana was the first European to travel the length of which of the world's famous rivers?
   a) Mississippi
   b) Amazon
   c) Rio Grande

10) Who was the first man to reach the South Pole?
   a) Captain Robert F. Scott
   b) Sir Ernest Shackleton
   c) Roald Amundsen

Answers: 1c, 2a, 3c, 4b, 5a, 6c, 7c, 8a, 9b, 10c

FAMOUS WOMEN

1) With what charitable work was the Quaker Elizabeth Fry associated?
   a) The abolition of slavery
   b) Prison reform
   c) Founding orphanages

2) Who wrote the children's classic *The Secret Garden*?
   a) Mrs Humphrey Ward
   b) Edith Nesbit
   c) Frances Hodgson Burnett

3) What was the Christian name of Mrs Beeton, author of *Mrs. Beeton's Book of Household Management*?
   a) Jane
   b) Elizabeth
   c) Isabella

4) Ada, Countess of Lovelace, an early pioneer of computing, was the daughter of which English romantic poet?
   a) Byron
   b) Shelley
   c) Keats

5) Who was the first American woman in space?
   a) Katherine Janeway
   b) Sally Ride
   c) Christa McAuliffe

GENIUS

6) Which queen's beautiful hair inspired Catullus and gave a star constellation its name?
   a) Zenobia
   b) Cleopatra
   c) Berenice

7) Of which actress did Dorothy Parker cruelly remark, 'She looks like something that would eat its young'?
   a) Peggy Ashcroft
   b) Edith Evans
   c) Margaret Rutherford

8) Which famous woman had a pet owl called Athena?
   a) Charlotte Brontë
   b) Queen Victoria
   c) Florence Nightingale

9) Of which country was Kim Campbell the first woman prime minister?
   a) Jamaica
   b) Canada
   c) Australia

10) Who was the first female to win the BBC Sports Personality of the Year award?
    a) The swimmer Anita Lonsborough
    b) The athlete Mary Rand
    c) The tennis player Ann Jones

Answers: 1b, 2c, 3c, 4a, 5b, 6c, 7b, 8c, 9b, 10a

'FIRSTS'

1) How did Charlotte Brew achieve a sporting first?
   a) First woman to swim the English Channel
   b) First woman to ride in the Grand National
   c) First woman to compete in the University Boat Race

2) Who was the first European explorer to cross the Antarctic Circle?
   a) Abel Tasman
   b) Ferdinand Magellan
   c) Captain James Cook

3) In 1901 what 'first' did the French writer Sully Prudhomme achieve?
   a) First living writer to have a novel adapted for film
   b) First writer to win the Nobel Prize for Literature
   c) First writer to serve as French ambassador to Britain

4) What 'first' did Margaret Gorman achieve in 1921 at the age of sixteen?
   a) First 'Miss America'
   b) First American swimmer to hold four world records simultaneously
   c) First solo female singer to record a hit single

5) Who was the first Secretary-General of the United Nations?
   a) Dag Hammarsjkold
   b) U Thant
   c) Trygve Lie

GENIUS

6) Who was the first black tennis player to win a Wimbledon title?
   a) Arthur Ashe
   b) Althea Gibson
   c) Serena Williams

7) What was the name of the airplane in which Charles Lindbergh made the first solo flight across the Atlantic?
   a) *Columbia*
   b) *Spirit of St. Louis*
   c) *Belle of New York*

8) Who was the first winner of the Oscar for Best Actor in 1927?
   a) John Barrymore
   b) Douglas Fairbanks Sr
   c) Emil Jannings

9) Who was the presenter of the first *Top of the Pops* programme?
   a) Jimmy Savile
   b) Tony Blackburn
   c) Kenny Everett

10) Which mountain was Edward Whymper the first to climb in 1865?
   a) Mt. McKinley
   b) The Matterhorn
   c) Mont Blanc

GENIUS

Answers: 1b, 2c, 3b, 4a, 5c, 6b, 7b, 8c, 9a, 10b

HUSBANDS AND WIVES

EXPERT

1) Which American dramatist was once the husband of Marilyn Monroe?
   a) Tennessee Williams
   b) Arthur Miller
   c) Eugene O'Neill

2) According to Chaucer, how many husbands did the Wife of Bath have 'at church door'?
   a) Three
   b) Four
   c) Five

3) Which classic English novel begins with the line, 'It is a truth universally acknowledged, that a single man in possession of a good fortune, must be in want of a wife'?
   a) *Tom Jones*
   b) *Great Expectations*
   c) *Pride and Prejudice*

4) Which two of Henry VIII's six wives survived him?
   a) Catherine Howard and Catherine Parr
   b) Catherine Parr and Anne of Cleves
   c) Catherine of Aragon and Anne of Cleves

5) Which famous couple, then husband and wife, starred in the 1966 film version of Edward Albee's play *Who's Afraid of Virginia Woolf*?
   a) Richard Burton and Elizabeth Taylor
   b) Laurence Olivier and Vivien Leigh
   c) Paul Newman and Joanne Woodward

6) In the Bible, what is the name of Abraham's wife?
   a) Rachel
   b) Sarah
   c) Leah

7) Who wrote the play *An Ideal Husband*?
   a) Oscar Wilde
   b) George Bernard Shaw
   c) J. M. Barrie

8) What profession do the husband and wife Roberto Alagna and Angela Gheorghiu share?
   a) They are both concert pianists
   b) They are both novelists
   c) They are both opera singers

9) Who wrote the Restoration drama *The Provok'd Wife*?
   a) William Congreve
   b) Sir John Vanbrugh
   c) Oliver Goldsmith

10) Which virtuoso musician was once the wife of the conductor and pianist Daniel Barenboim?
   a) Sidonie Goossens
   b) Jacqueline Du Pré
   c) Evelyn Glennie

EXPERT

Answers: 1b, 2c, 3c, 4b, 5a, 6b, 7a, 8c, 9b, 10b

INITIALS

Some famous people are best known by their initials rather than their Christian names. What do the initials in these names stand for?

EXPERT

1) J. K. Rowling
   a) Joanne Kathleen
   b) Jane Kathleen
   c) Joanne Karen

2) W. G. Grace
   a) William George
   b) William Gustav
   c) William Gilbert

3) M. C. Escher
   a) Matthias Cornelis
   b) Maurits Carl
   c) Maurits Cornelis

4) J. R. R. Tolkien
   a) John Ronald Reuel
   b) John Reginald Richard
   c) James Reginald Robert

5) O. J. Simpson
   a) Orris John
   b) Oscar Jethro
   c) Orenthal James

6) **K. D. Lang**
   a) Karen Denise
   b) Kathryn Dawn
   c) Kathryn Diane

7) **T. E. Lawrence**
   a) Thomas Edward
   b) Thomas Edgar
   c) Thomas Eldred

8) **J. D. Salinger**
   a) John David
   b) Jerome David
   c) Jacob Darius

9) **C. P. E. Bach**
   a) Casper Philip Erich
   b) Carl Philip Emmanuel
   c) Carsten Peter Emmanuel

10) **G. K. Chesterton**
   a) Gilbert Keith
   b) George Kenneth
   c) Graham Kenneth

EXPERT

Answers: 1a, 2c, 3c, 4a, 5c, 6b, 7a, 8b, 9b, 10a

NICKNAMES

Who were sometimes known by the following nicknames or aliases?

EXPERT

1) **The Iron Duke**
   a) The Duke of Marlborough
   b) The Duke of Wellington
   c) The Duke of Devonshire

2) **The Boston Strangler**
   a) Albert De Salvo
   b) Vincent Gigante
   c) Charles Luciano

3) **The Illinois Baboon**
   a) Abraham Lincoln
   b) George Washington
   c) Ulysses S. Grant

4) **Attila the Hen**
   a) Indira Gandhi
   b) Ann Widdecombe
   c) Margaret Thatcher

5) **The It Girl**
   a) Gloria Swanson
   b) Clara Bow
   c) Mary Pickford

6) Satchmo
   a) Louis Armstrong
   b) Charlie Parker
   c) John Coltrane

7) Buffalo Bill
   a) Samuel Colt
   b) William Hickok
   c) William F. Cody

8) Bloody Mary
   a) Mary Magdalene
   b) Mary, Queen of Scots
   c) Mary Tudor

EXPERT

9) The Desert Fox
   a) T. E. Lawrence
   b) Viscount Montgomery
   c) Erwin Rommel

10) Calamity Jane
   a) Martha Jane Cannary
   b) Jane Carlyle
   c) Mary Jane Kopechne

Answers: 1b, 2a, 3a, 4c, 5b, 6a, 7c, 8c, 9c, 10a

PARENTS AND CHILDREN

EXPERT

1) Which Russian author wrote the novel *Fathers and Sons*?
   a) Dostoevsky
   b) Turgenev
   c) Tolstoy

2) Who was the father of the Black Prince, hero of the English victories over the French at Crecy and Poitiers in 1346 and 1356?
   a) Henry III
   b) Edward II
   c) Edward III

3) Which movie star has a son called Satchel?
   a) Tom Hanks
   b) Woody Allen
   c) Robert Downey Jr

4) The daughter of which Hollywood movie star wrote a memoir called *Mommie Dearest*?
   a) Joan Crawford
   b) Bette Davis
   c) Katherine Hepburn

5) Which of the following writers was the daughter of Lord and Lady Redesdale?
   a) Virginia Woolf
   b) Nancy Mitford
   c) Edith Sitwell

6) What was the name of Sigmund Freud's youngest daughter, the only one of his children to follow him into the profession of psychoanalysis?
   a) Anna
   b) Mariana
   c) Helena

7) Which French novel begins, 'Mother died today. Or, maybe, yesterday; I can't be sure'?
   a) Michel Houellebecq's *Atomised*
   b) Jean-Paul Sartre's *Nausea*
   c) Albert Camus's *The Outsider*

8) The mother of James I was Mary, Queen of Scots. Who was his father?
   a) Francis II of France
   b) Earl of Bothwell
   c) Lord Darnley

9) Which English writer wrote a play called *A Voyage Round My Father*?
   a) John Mortimer
   b) Alan Bennett
   c) Tom Stoppard

10) Which saint was the mother of the Emperor Constantine?
   a) St. Teresa of Avila
   b) St. Veronica
   c) St. Helena

Answers: 1b, 2c, 3b, 4a, 5b, 6a, 7c, 8c, 9a, 10c

PEOPLE 1

1) Where was Napoleon born?
   a) Sicily
   b) Sardinia
   c) Corsica

2) What was the first name of the British composer Vaughan Williams?
   a) Ralph
   b) Edward
   c) Thomas

NOVICE

3) Which famous Italian gave his name to a biscuit?
   a) Garibaldi
   b) Leonardo da Vinci
   c) Rossini

4) Who was British Prime Minister at the outbreak of World War II?
   a) Winston Churchill
   b) Harold Macmillan
   c) Neville Chamberlain

5) Which writer of detective stories mysteriously disappeared for 11 days in 1926?
   a) Sir Arthur Conan Doyle
   b) Agatha Christie
   c) Dorothy L. Sayers

NOVICE

6) Which American sportsman was nicknamed 'The Brown Bomber'?
   a) Muhammad Ali
   b) Joe Louis
   c) Jesse Owens

7) What nationality was the founder of psychoanalysis, Sigmund Freud?
   a) German
   b) Swiss
   c) Austrian

8) Which poet kept a pet bear when he was at Cambridge University?
   a) Byron
   b) Tennyson
   c) Wordsworth

9) On which musical instrument was Andres Segovia a famous virtuoso?
   a) Piano
   b) Trumpet
   c) Guitar

10) Which of the following statements is true of the nineteenth century politician William Huskisson?
   a) He was the illegitimate son of George IV
   b) He was the first person killed in a railway accident
   c) He was blinded in a childhood accident

Answers: 1c, 2a, 3a, 4c, 5b, 6b, 7c, 8a, 9c, 10b

PEOPLE 2

1) Who was the last British Viceroy of India?
   a) Lord Curzon
   b) Lord Mountbatten
   c) Lord Cardigan

2) In which century was the composer Johann Sebastian Bach born?
   a) 16th
   b) 17th
   c) 18th

NOVICE

3) In which branch of science did Edwin Hubble achieve success?
   a) Physics
   b) Biology
   c) Astronomy

4) Who partnered Annie Lennox in the 1980s group Eurhythmics?
   a) Dave Stewart
   b) Stewart Davidson
   c) Dave Davies

5) What did Colonel Thomas Blood attempt to steal in 1671?
   a) The skull of Oliver Cromwell
   b) The *Mona Lisa*
   c) The Crown Jewels

6) Which actor was critically acclaimed for his performance in *Shine*?
   a) David Garrick
   b) Anthony Hopkins
   c) Geoffrey Rush

7) As what is John Galliano famous?
   a) Fashion designer
   b) Footballer
   c) Artist

8) What was the first name of the suffragette, Mrs Pankhurst?
   a) Emma
   b) Emily
   c) Emmeline

9) Who died in 1798, at a castle in Bavaria where he was working as a librarian?
   a) Rousseau
   b) Casanova
   c) Voltaire

10) In which country was the jeweller Fabergé born?
   a) France
   b) Belgium
   c) Russia

NOVICE

Answers: 1b, 2b, 3c, 4a, 5c, 6c, 7a, 8c, 9b, 10c

PEOPLE 3

1) Who was Soviet Foreign Minister from 1957 to 1985?
   a) Leonid Brezhnev
   b) Andrei Gromyko
   c) Konstantin Chernenko

2) In whose memory did Don McLean write the song
   American Pie?
   a) Elvis Presley
   b) Eddie Cochrane
   c) Buddy Holly

EXPERT

3) What nationality is the former Secretary General of the
   UN, Boutros Boutros-Ghali?
   a) Egyptian
   b) Greek
   c) Algerian

4) What was the name of the South African surgeon who
   performed the world's first open heart transplant in 1967?
   a) Dr Christian Barnard
   b) Dr Ali Bacher
   c) Dr Richard Vorster

5) In which century was Martin Luther born?
   a) 15th
   b) 16th
   c) 17th

6) Who was the first Director-General of the BBC?
   a) John Buchan
   b) John Galsworthy
   c) John Reith

7) How was Jean-Baptiste Poquelin better known?
   a) Nostradamus
   b) Molière
   c) Voltaire

8) Which famous name of the Wild West was shot and killed whilst playing poker in a Deadwood saloon?
   a) Billy the Kid
   b) Jesse James
   c) Wild Bill Hickok

EXPERT

9) Of what was Sir John Houblon the first Governor?
   a) New South Wales
   b) The Bank of England
   c) Dartmoor Prison

10) Which British Prime Minister took to bricklaying as a hobby?
   a) Harold Wilson
   b) Anthony Eden
   c) Winston Churchill

Answers: 1b, 2c, 3a, 4a, 5a, 6c, 7b, 8c, 9b, 10c

PEOPLE 4

1) Who was the first Astronomer Royal?
   a) John Flamsteed
   b) William Herschel
   c) Edmund Halley

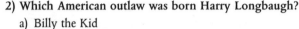

2) Which American outlaw was born Harry Longbaugh?
   a) Billy the Kid
   b) The Ringo Kid
   c) The Sundance Kid

GENIUS

3) Who lived at Strawberry Hill, Twickenham?
   a) Horace Walpole
   b) Charles Dickens
   c) Alexander Pope

4) In which game was Howard Staunton a world champion in the 19th century?
   a) Bridge
   b) Billiards
   c) Chess

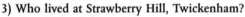

5) What useful household object was first invented and patented by William Lyman in 1870?
   a) The sewing machine
   b) The can-opener
   c) The screw-top lid

6) Whose first published book was called *How to Cheat at Cooking*?
   a) Nigella Lawson
   b) Delia Smith
   c) Barbara Cartland

7) Which 19th century banker became the first practising Jewish MP in the House of Commons?
   a) Benjamin Disraeli
   b) Baron Lionel Nathan de Rothschild
   c) Moses Montefiore

8) How was Marie Grosholtz better known?
   a) Queen Marie of Roumania
   b) Madame Tussaud
   c) Sarah Bernhardt

9) Which composer used to hold his chin with his left hand and conduct with his right because he was afraid his head would fall off?
   a) Tchaikovsky
   b) Richard Strauss
   c) Beethoven

10) Which French novelist lived for a year in Upper Norwood in south London at the end of the nineteenth century?
   a) Marcel Proust
   b) Emile Zola
   c) Victor Hugo

Answers: 1a, 2c, 3a, 4c, 5b, 6b, 7b, 8b, 9a, 10b

GENIUS

QUOTATIONS

Who is being described in the following quotations?

1) 'Mad, bad and dangerous to know'
   a) Napoleon
   b) Lord Byron
   c) Oscar Wilde

2) 'He is a man suffering from petrified adolescence'
   a) Adolf Hitler
   b) Franklin Roosevelt
   c) Winston Churchill

3) 'Whatsoever he penned, he never blotted out a line'
   a) John Milton
   b) Charles Dickens
   c) William Shakespeare

4) 'A modest little man with much to be modest about'
   a) Clement Attlee
   b) David Lloyd George
   c) Stanley Baldwin

5) 'He speaks to me as if I was a public meeting'
   a) William Gladstone
   b) Benjamin Disraeli
   c) Lord Tennyson

6) 'This siren, this goat-footed bard, this half-human visitor to our age from the hag-ridden magic and enchanted woods of Celtic antiquity'
   a) Dylan Thomas
   b) Ramsay MacDonald
   c) David Lloyd-George

7) 'You always knew where you stood with him because he always let you down'
   a) John Barrymore
   b) Dylan Thomas
   c) Errol Flynn

8) 'He has out-soared the shadow of our night'
   a) Samuel Taylor Coleridge
   b) John Keats
   c) William Wordsworth

9) 'She was good at playing abstract confusion in the same way a midget is good at being short'
   a) Marilyn Monroe
   b) Doris Day
   c) Judy Garland

10) 'He was a good man but did not know how to paint'
    a) John Constable
    b) Michelangelo
    c) Picasso

GENIUS

Answers: 1b, 2c, 3c, 4a, 5a, 6c, 7c, 8b, 9a, 10b

SAINTS AND SINNERS

1) **Who is the patron saint of travellers?**
   a) St. Brendan
   b) St. Paul
   c) St. Christopher

2) **For what crime was Al Capone jailed in 1931?**
   a) Murder
   b) Tax evasion
   c) Gun running

EXPERT

3) **In which century was St. Francis of Assisi born?**
   a) 11th
   b) 12th
   c) 13th

4) **What was the name of Dr Crippen's mistress, with whom he fled Britain after murdering his wife?**
   a) Ethel Le Neve
   b) Edith Thompson
   c) Belle Elmore

5) **Which saint wrote *City of God*?**
   a) St. Augustine
   b) St. Thomas Aquinas
   c) St. Jerome

EXPERT

6) **Where was Mother Teresa born?**
   a) Bucharest, Romania
   b) Skopje, Macedonia
   c) Tirana, Albania

7) **Whom did the anarchist Leon Czolgosz assassinate in 1901?**
   a) US President William McKinley
   b) King Umberto I of Italy
   c) Empress Elisabeth of Austria

8) **Which saint had a vision of the Virgin Mary at Lourdes in 1858?**
   a) St. Clare
   b) St. Theresa
   c) St. Bernardette

9) **What was the name of Ronnie and Reggie Kray's elder brother?**
   a) Charles
   b) Frank
   c) Robert

10) **Which American criminal is the subject of Norman Mailer's book *The Executioner's Song*?**
   a) Charles Manson
   b) Gary Gilmore
   c) Lee Harvey Oswald

Answers: 1c, 2b, 3b, 4a, 5a, 6b, 7a, 8c, 9a, 10b

WHAT ARE THEY REMEMBERED FOR?

For what are the following people chiefly remembered?

GENIUS

1) **Johan Vaaler**
   a) Writing works of Protestant theology
   b) Inventing the paper clip
   c) Discovering the planet Uranus

2) **Ludwig Leichhardt**
   a) Exploring Australia
   b) Establishing the first kindergarten
   c) Founding Berlin's Zoological Gardens

3) **Mildred and Patty Hill**
   a) Composing the tune now known as 'Happy Birthday to You'
   b) Writing the words to the carol *Away in a Manger*
   c) Working with the Pankhursts in the Suffragette movement

4) **Rafael Sabatini**
   a) Writing swashbuckling historical fiction
   b) Leading Italian resistance to Mussolini
   c) Founding the art movement known as 'Futurism'

5) **Michel Bégon**
   a) Devising three important mathematical theorems
   b) Starring in a series of French comedy films
   c) Giving his name to the Begonia

6) Coleman Hawkins
   a) Founding a chain of American department stores
   b) Playing jazz saxophone
   c) Holding the record for most home runs in a season in baseball

7) Lord Hawke
   a) Serving as Home Secretary in Gladstone's government of 1869–1874
   b) Defeating the French in a battle during the Peninsular War
   c) Captaining Yorkshire and England at cricket

8) Alfred Austin
   a) Succeeding Lord Tennyson as poet laureate
   b) Inventing the carpet sweeper
   c) Discovering the link between malaria and mosquitoes

9) Mary Seacole
   a) Qualifying as the first female doctor in Great Britain
   b) Nursing soldiers in the Crimean War
   c) Becoming the first elected female mayor in Great Britain

10) Ludwig von Köchel
   a) Conducting the Berlin Symphony Orchestra
   b) Composing the music for Hollywood films
   c) Cataloguing the works of Mozart

GENIUS

Answers: 1b, 2a, 3a, 4a, 5c, 6b, 7c, 8a, 9b, 10c

SCIENCE, ASTRONOMY AND NUMBERS

ASTRONOMY

1) Where are the Galilean moons, discovered by Galileo in 1609, to be found?
   a) Orbiting Mars
   b) Orbiting Saturn
   c) Orbiting Jupiter

2) Which astronomical term derives its name from the Ancient Greek word for 'milk'?
   a) Comet
   b) Galaxy
   c) Moon

EXPERT

3) What is the Cassini Division?
   a) Another name for the asteroid belt
   b) A gap between two of the rings of Saturn
   c) The distance between two stars in the constellation Orion

4) Which of the planets in the solar system was discovered in 1846 by the German astronomer Johann Galle?
   a) Neptune
   b) Pluto
   c) Uranus

5) Other than the sun, what is the nearest star to the earth?
   a) Proxima Centauri
   b) Sirius
   c) Procyon

6) In which constellation can you see the two stars Rigel and Betelgeuse?
   a) Gemini
   b) Leo
   c) Orion

7) What is unusual about the asteroid Vesta?
   a) It's on a course to collide with the Earth in 12 million years time
   b) It's the only asteroid that can occasionally be seen with the naked eye
   c) It's the smallest asteroid so far discovered

8) Which comet could be seen from Earth in March 1997?
   a) Hale-Bopp
   b) Halley's
   c) Shoemaker-Levy

9) What is the brightest star in the night sky?
   a) Sirius
   b) Rigel
   c) Arcturus

10) What is the name of Pluto's only moon?
   a) Phobos
   b) Triton
   c) Charon

EXPERT

Answers: 1c, 2b, 3b, 4a, 5a, 6c, 7b, 8a, 9a, 10c

BIOLOGY

1) What does a herpetologist study?
   a) Reptiles
   b) Skin diseases
   c) Bats

2) What is the everyday name for the plants that have the scientific classification *Gramineae?*
   a) Ferns
   b) Grasses
   c) Cacti

3) Bile is secreted by which human organ?
   a) Liver
   b) Gall bladder
   c) Pancreas

4) Which vessels carry blood towards the heart?
   a) Capillaries
   b) Veins
   c) Arteries

5) How many bones are there in a fully developed human skeleton?
   a) 156
   b) 176
   c) 206

6) What is the common name for *Drosophila melanogaster*, a creature much used in genetic experiments?
   a) Fruit fly
   b) Earthworm
   c) Blowfly

7) Of what is morphology the study?
   a) DNA replication
   b) The effects of sleep-inducing drugs
   c) The shape of plants and animals

8) Which biological process was first discovered by Jan Ingenshousz in the 18th century?
   a) Asexual reproduction
   b) Photosynthesis
   c) Cell replication

9) What does the peptide bond link together?
   a) Human body cells
   b) Enzymes
   c) Amino acids

10) What is a gamete?
   a) A cell connected with blood circulation
   b) A cell connected with digestion
   c) A cell connected with reproduction

NOVICE

Answers: 1a, 2b, 3a, 4b, 5c, 6a, 7c, 8b, 9c, 10c

CALENDARS

EXPERT

1) Which day of the week was named for the Scandinavian goddess of love?
   a) Monday for Mona
   b) Wednesday for Wotan
   c) Friday for Frigga or Freya

2) In the year 46 BC who ordered a reform of the calendar?
   a) Alexander the Great
   b) Julius Caesar
   c) Ptolemy VII, Pharaoh of Egypt

3) Which month was named for the Roman God of War?
   a) March
   b) May
   c) July

4) Which month was the seventh month of the Roman calendar?
   a) July
   b) August
   c) September

5) Which feast in the Christian calendar is also known as the Twelfth Day of Christmas?
   a) Advent
   b) Epiphany
   c) The Circumcision of our Lord

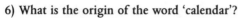

6) What is the origin of the word 'calendar'?
   a) Kalendarium from the Latin word for accounting books
   b) Kalendae or calends was the first day of each month in the ancient Roman calendar
   c) The Norman French word 'calender' meaning 'a month'

7) After which historical figure is the Gregorian calendar named?
   a) Pope Gregory XIII
   b) Gregorius Thomas Ziegler, Bishop of Linz
   c) The historian Gregory of Tours

8) The Gregorian calendar was first introduced to Europe in 1585. When did Britain fall into line and adopt it?
   a) 1586
   b) 1653
   c) 1752

9) In which calendar were years counted from the accession of an emperor until 1911 AD?
   a) Chinese
   b) Indian
   c) Japanese

10) Which day of the week was named after the Norse god of thunder?
   a) Tuesday
   b) Thursday
   c) Saturday

EXPERT

Answers: 1c, 2b, 3a, 4c, 5b, 6b, 7a, 8c, 9a, 10b

CHEMISTRY

EXPERT

1) Which chemical element has the atomic number 78 and the chemical symbol Pt?
   a) Potassium
   b) Platinum
   c) Lead

2) How was phosphorus first discovered in 1674?
   a) By subtracting salt from ocean water
   b) By distilling human urine
   c) By drying fish

3) What is 'dry ice'?
   a) Frozen carbon dioxide
   b) Ordinary ice from which all moisture has been removed
   c) Frozen sulphur dioxide

4) Which of the following elements is one of the so-called 'noble gases'?
   a) Chlorine
   b) Fluorine
   c) Argon

5) Which of the following elements is a liquid at room temperature?
   a) Sulphur
   b) Tungsten
   c) Bromine

6) Which chemist first devised the Periodic Table, supposedly after seeing its basic structure in a dream?
   a) Sir Humphrey Davy
   b) Dmitriy Mendeleyev
   c) Antoine Lavoisier

7) How did the 18th century French chemist Antoine Lavoisier die?
   a) He was killed in a duel
   b) He inhaled poisonous gases during an experiment
   c) He was guillotined during the French Revolution

EXPERT

8) What is the single letter chemical symbol for Tungsten?
   a) W
   b) T
   c) K

9) Which is the lightest of the chemical elements?
   a) Helium
   b) Oxygen
   c) Hydrogen

10) What type of solution turns litmus paper red?
   a) Alkaline solution
   b) Acid solution
   c) Neutral solution

Answers: 1b, 2b, 3a, 4c, 5c, 6b, 7c, 8a, 9c, 10b

COMPUTING

1) How many bits are there in a byte?
   a) 4
   b) 8
   c) 24

2) Of what is the word 'pixel' an abbreviation?
   a) picture element
   b) pixillated element
   c) pictographic element

 NOVICE

3) Who co-founded Apple Computer with Steve Jobs in 1976?
   a) Steve Wozniak
   b) Bill Gates
   c) Jaron Lanier

4) In computing what does URL stand for?
   a) Universal Resource Language
   b) Uniform Resource Locator
   c) Uniform Research Locator

5) What was the name of the first electronic computer?
   a) ENIAC
   b) MANIAC
   c) SANIAC

6) What type of software package is Microsoft Excel?
   a) Spreadsheet
   b) Word processing
   c) Virus protection

7) Which of the following is an operating system?
   a) Napster
   b) Microsoft Works
   c) Linux

8) In which country was the 19th century computer pioneer Charles Babbage born?
   a) Ireland
   b) England
   c) Scotland

9) For which organisation was Tim Berners-Lee working when he created the bases of the World Wide Web?
   a) Ministry of Defence
   b) IBM
   c) CERN (European Laboratory for Particle Physics)

10 In computing what does SMTP stand for?
   a) Special Mail Transfer Protocol
   b) Standard Mail Transfer Protocol
   c) Simple Mail Transfer Protocol

NOVICE

Answers: 1b, 2a, 3a, 4b, 5a, 6a, 7c, 8b, 9c, 10c

CONSTELLATIONS

1) Which cluster of stars is also called 'The Seven Sisters'?
   a) Lyra
   b) Orion's Belt
   c) The Pleiades

2) In which constellation is the star Vega?
   a) Lyra
   b) Leda
   c) Leo

GENIUS

3) What does the constellation Cetus represent?
   a) A serpent
   b) A maiden
   c) A whale

4) Which of these stars is joined with Vega and Altair to form 'The Summer Triangle'?
   a) Betelgeuse
   b) Polaris
   c) Deneb

5) Which constellation is also known as 'The Plough'?
   a) Ursa Minor
   b) Ursa Major
   c) Bootes

6) How are the stars Alnilam, Alnitak and Mintaka better known?
   a) Orion's Belt
   b) Ursa Minor
   c) Pegasus

7) Which star is 'the eye of Taurus'?
   a) Betelgeuse
   b) Polaris
   c) Aldebaran

8) How many constellations are officially listed by the International Astronomical Union?
   a) 48
   b) 68
   c) 88

GENIUS

9) Which constellation is named after the woman whom Perseus, in Greek mythology, rescued from a sea monster?
   a) Andromeda
   b) Cassiopeia
   c) Virgo

10) In which constellation is the Horsehead Nebula?
   a) Taurus
   b) Orion
   c) Pegasus

Answers: 1c, 2a, 3c, 4c, 5b, 6a, 7c, 8c, 9a, 10b

DINOSAURS

NOVICE

1) What does the name 'dinosaur' mean?
   a) Great monster
   b) Terrible lizard
   c) Fire dragon

2) Which of the following dinosaurs was not a meat-eater?
   a) Tyrannosaurus Rex
   b) Deinonychus
   c) Stegosaurus

3) What is the scientific name for fossilised dinosaur droppings?
   a) Cacoliths
   b) Scatolites
   c) Coprolites

4) Which of the following dinosaurs had a very long neck?
   a) Brachiosaurus
   b) Pteranodon
   c) Triceratops

5) For approximately how long did dinosaurs rule the earth?
   a) 75 million years
   b) 175 million years
   c) 275 million years

6) What colour was the skin of most dinosaurs?
   a) Green
   b) Grey
   c) We don't know

7) In which year was the word dinosaur first coined?
   a) 1795
   b) 1842
   c) 1881

8) Which is the smallest dinosaur so far discovered?
   a) Allosaurus
   b) Pteranodon
   c) Composognathus

9) Where would Ichthyosaurs have been found?
   a) In the sea
   b) On land
   c) In the air

10) Which dinosaur's name means 'three-horned face'?
   a) Diplodocus
   b) Triceratops
   c) Brontosaurus

NOVICE

Answers: 1b, 2c, 3c, 4a, 5b, 6c, 7b, 8c, 9a, 10b

FAMOUS SCIENTISTS

EXPERT

1) **In which English county was Sir Isaac Newton born?**
   a) Yorkshire
   b) Lincolnshire
   c) Essex

2) **Which German scientist is famous for his 'uncertainty principle'?**
   a) Erwin Schrodinger
   b) Max Planck
   c) Werner Heisenberg

3) **Who was the first woman scientist to win a Nobel Prize?**
   a) Rosalind Franklin
   b) Marie Curie
   c) Dorothy Hodgkins

4) **Where did Murray Gell-Mann find the word 'quark' which he used as a name for a type of sub-atomic particle?**
   a) In James Joyce's novel *Finnegans Wake*
   b) In a cookbook
   c) In a German dictionary

5) **In which element did the French scientist Henri Becquerel first discover naturally occurring radioactivity?**
   a) Radium
   b) Plutonium
   c) Uranium

6) Which discovery in medicine was made by the 17th century English physician William Harvey?
   a) The existence of bacteria
   b) The circulation of the blood
   c) The anaesthetic properties of ether

7) What was the occupation of Gregor Mendel, whose scientific work became the basis for modern genetics?
   a) He was a monk
   b) He was a doctor
   c) He was a lawyer

EXPERT

8) In which century did Copernicus first publish his ideas about the earth moving around the sun?
   a) 15th
   b) 16th
   c) 17th

9) In which field was the Victorian polymath Charles Babbage a pioneer?
   a) Transplant surgery
   b) Genetics
   c) Computing

10) In which German city was Albert Einstein born in 1879?
   a) Bonn
   b) Ulm
   c) Munich

Answers: 1b, 2c, 3b, 4a, 5c, 6b, 7a, 8b, 9c, 10b

GENERAL SCIENCE 1

1) Which metal is extracted from bauxite?
   a) Lead
   b) Tin
   c) Aluminium

2) Which vitamin deficiency causes scurvy?
   a) Vitamin C
   b) Vitamin D
   c) Vitamin B

NOVICE

3) Which element has the chemical symbol Sn?
   a) Antimony
   b) Tin
   c) Selenium

4) What does an ichthyologist study?
   a) Reptiles
   b) Beetles
   c) Fish

5) What causes the Tyndall Effect?
   a) Light
   b) Heat
   c) Sound

6) What is 'nutation'?
   a) A method of measuring the speed at which stars are travelling away from us
   b) A small variation in the spinning of the Earth on its axis
   c) A type of mammalian hibernation

7) In which decade of the 20th century was the 'Big Bang' theory of the universe first proposed?
   a) 1920s
   b) 1940s
   c) 1960s

8) Which of the following words means the ability of a liquid to resist flowing?
   a) Viscosity
   b) Fluidity
   c) Penetrability

9) Which of the following is the standard unit of measurement for measuring force?
   a) Newton
   b) Joule
   c) Watt

10) What kind of plant is an epiphyte?
   a) One with exceptionally speedy growth
   b) A non-parasitic growth on another plant
   c) One which grows towards a light source

NOVICE

Answers: 1c, 2a, 3b, 4c, 5a, 6b, 7a, 8a, 9a, 10b

GENERAL SCIENCE 2

EXPERT

1) What is the scientific term for plants such as cacti which live where it is difficult to obtain water?
   a) Hydrophytes
   b) Mesophytes
   c) Xerophytes

2) Which element makes up 78% of the Earth's atmosphere?
   a) Argon
   b) Nitrogen
   c) Oxygen

3) What does a pyrometer measure?
   a) High temperatures
   b) Low temperatures
   c) Light intensity

4) Which system in the body do enzymes affect?
   a) Reproductive
   b) Digestive
   c) Circulatory

5) Which of the following rocks will float in water?
   a) Basalt
   b) Pumice
   c) Obsidian

6) To which of the following do Messier numbers refer?
   a) Elements in the Periodic Table
   b) Sub-atomic particles
   c) Star clusters

7) What metal is extracted from hematite ore?
   a) Iron
   b) Lead
   c) Tin

8) From what or whom does the element Strontium derive its name?
   a) A Norwegian chemist
   b) A German word for 'heavy'
   c) A village in Argyllshire

EXPERT

9) Which acid is also known as oil of vitriol?
   a) Sulphuric acid
   b) Hydrochloric acid
   c) Nitric acid

10) What is the correct scientific term for the nostrils?
   a) The philtrum
   b) The nares
   c) The cochlea

Answers: 1c, 2b, 3a, 4b, 5b, 6c, 7a, 8c, 9a, 10b

GENERAL SCIENCE 3

1) **What are produced by the endocrine glands?**
   a) Hormones
   b) Red blood cells
   c) White blood cells

2) **What is the SI unit of resistance?**
   a) Ohm
   b) Volt
   c) Ampere

3) **What is measured by a hygrometer?**
   a) Pressure
   b) Humidity
   c) Force

4) **Of what are meiosis and mitosis both processes?**
   a) Cell division
   b) Liquid absorption
   c) Human digestion

5) **If a chemical solution is neutral, what is its pH?**
   a) 4
   b) 7
   c) 12

EXPERT

6) Where in the body would you find the Island of Langerhans?
   a) Liver
   b) Pancreas
   c) Ear

7) At which temperature are the Celsius and Fahrenheit scales the same?
   a) −40
   b) −32
   c) zero

EXPERT

8) Which of the following is another name for specific gravity?
   a) Relative density
   b) Gravitational force
   c) Quantum pull

9) What function do chloroplasts perform in plants?
   a) They harness the sun's energy
   b) They enable plants to produce fruits
   c) They process waste

10) What is the SI unit of pressure?
   a) Newton
   b) Joule
   c) Pascal

Answers: 1a, 2a, 3b, 4a, 5b, 6b, 7a, 8a, 9a, 10c

GEOLOGY

EXPERT

1) In geology, what is the wearing away of rock and soil by the action of water, ice, wind and gravity known as?
   a) Extrusion
   b) Erosion
   c) Lithification

2) What are the three main types of rock?
   a) Crystalline, mineral, sedimentary
   b) Igneous, metamorphic, sedimentary
   c) Sand, clay, gravel

3) What are the two most abundant elements in the Earth's crust?
   a) Sodium and nitrogen
   b) Carbon and potassium
   c) Silicon and oxygen

4) Batholiths are composed mostly of what type of rock?
   a) Granite
   b) Basalt
   c) Limestone

5) What are fumaroles?
   a) Holes or vents from which steam rushes into the air
   b) Thermal areas full of water-saturated sediment
   c) Hot springs that erupt periodically

6) In which one of the following types of rock can fossils be found?
   a) Metamorphic rock
   b) Sedimentary rock
   c) Igneous rock

7) Which type of coal is considered a metamorphic rock?
   a) Lignite
   b) Anthracite
   c) Bituminous

8) Which of the following is the softest on the Mohs scale of relative mineral hardness?
   a) Talc
   b) Gypsum
   c) Topaz

EXPERT

9) Who was the German scientist who first proposed the theory of 'continental drift'?
   a) Harry Hess
   b) Max Muller
   c) Alfred Wegener

10) Which of these is a high grade metamorphic rock?
   a) Gneiss
   b) Limestone
   c) Granite

Answers: 1b, 2b, 3c, 4a, 5a, 6b, 7b, 8a, 9c, 10a

INVENTIONS AND INVENTORS

1) In which country was paper first invented and used?
   a) Egypt
   b) India
   c) China

2) What was invented in 1644 by Evangelista Torricelli?
   a) The mercury barometer
   b) An air freshener
   c) The thermometer

NOVICE

3) Which inventor was known as 'The Wizard of Menlo Park'?
   a) Thomas Edison
   b) Alexander Graham Bell
   c) Eli Whitney

4) With which form of transport is the name of the British inventor Richard Trevithick associated?
   a) Cars
   b) Planes
   c) Trains

5) In 1834 who designed what he called 'the analytical engine', the forerunner of the modern electronic computer?
   a) Michael Faraday
   b) Charles Babbage
   c) J. J. Thomson

6) For what invention is Wallace Carothers remembered?
   a) Nylon
   b) Velcro
   c) Rayon

7) Who invented the Kodak camera?
   a) Arthur Kodak
   b) Thomas Edison
   c) George Eastman

8) When William Semple invented chewing gum in 1869, for what did he intend it to be used?
   a) As a means of exercising the jaw
   b) As a glue for household use
   c) As bait to catch birds

NOVICE

9) For what discovery is Clarence Birdseye remembered?
   a) The planet Pluto
   b) Devising a practical method of freezing food
   c) The world's first colour photograph

10) When was the first lawn mower invented?
   a) 1888
   b) 1607
   c) 1830

Answers: 1c, 2a, 3a, 4c, 5b, 6a, 7c, 8a, 9b, 10c

MATHEMATICS

EXPERT

1) What is a triangle with three sides of different lengths called?
   a) An isosceles triangle
   b) A scalene triangle
   c) A congruent triangle

2) What were Napier's Bones?
   a) An early form of calculating machine
   b) Drawing tools for use in geometry
   c) A binary system

3) Which Greek letter is used in mathematics to represent the ratio of a circle's circumference to its diameter?
   a) φ
   b) π
   c) ρ

4) In which ancient country was the concept of zero first developed?
   a) India
   b) Egypt
   c) Greece

5) The 19th-century mathematician Galois died at the age of 20. How did he die?
   a) In a shipwreck
   b) In a riding accident
   c) In a duel

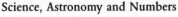

6) What is the square root of 324?
   a) 17
   b) 18
   c) 22

7) What is the name given to the formula $a^2 + b^2 = c^2$?
   a) The quadratic formula
   b) The Pythagorean formula
   c) Einstein's formula

8) If two angles are complementary, to what do they add up?
   a) 90 degrees
   b) 180 degrees
   c) 360 degrees

EXPERT

9) In which branch of maths would you find a phenomenon known as the Witch of Agnesi?
   a) Topology
   b) Algebra
   c) Geometry

10) Which of the following is a prime number?
   a) 53
   b) 63
   c) 93

Answers: 1b, 2a, 3b, 4a, 5c, 6b, 7b, 8a, 9c, 10a

MEDICINE 1

1) What is the chief symptom of the visual disorder known as diplopia?
   a) Seeing spots before the eyes
   b) Blindness
   c) Double vision

2) What are the only cells that never re-grow?
   a) Bone
   b) Brain
   c) Bone marrow

3) When was the first operation performed under general anaesthetic?
   a) 1818
   b) 1842
   c) 1900

4) What did Karl Landsteiner discover in 1909?
   a) The function of the pancreas
   b) The blood groups A, B and O
   c) The normal human temperature of 98.6 °F

5) How is the medical condition lateral epicondylitis better known?
   a) Tennis Elbow
   b) Housemaid's Knee
   c) Writer's Cramp

6) Where in the body could you find the anvil and the stirrup?
   a) In the brain
   b) In the foot
   c) In the ear

7) The disease rickets is caused by a deficiency of which vitamin?
   a) D
   b) C
   c) B

8) From which plant is the drug *digitalis* obtained?
   a) Deadly nightshade
   b) Poppy
   c) Foxglove

9) Which essential piece of medical equipment was invented by T. H. Laennec in 1816?
   a) The thermometer
   b) The stethoscope
   c) The syringe

10) Which Greek physician is known as the 'Father of Medicine'?
   a) Hippocrates
   b) Galen
   c) Aristotle

NOVICE

Answers: 1c, 2b, 3b, 4b, 5a, 6c, 7a, 8c, 9b, 10a

MEDICINE 2

1) What is the more common name for the disease varicella?
   a) German measles
   b) Mumps
   c) Chicken-pox

2) Which part of the human body is also called the axilla?
   a) The elbow
   b) The armpit
   c) The shoulder

EXPERT

3) Which viral disease takes its name from a river in the Republic of Congo?
   a) Yellow fever
   b) Ebola
   c) Dengue fever

4) Which painkiller was first patented in 1899?
   a) Paracetamol
   b) Codeine
   c) Aspirin

5) Which English physician coined the word 'vaccination' to describe a method of inoculation he was using?
   a) William Harvey
   b) Edward Jenner
   c) Lord Lister

6) In which century did the first blood transfusion take place?
   a) 17th
   b) 18th
   c) 19th

7) Which of these human organs was the first to be successfully transplanted?
   a) Kidney
   b) Liver
   c) Heart

8) For which disease did Jonas Salk discover a vaccine in 1955?
   a) Polio
   b) Tuberculosis
   c) Malaria

9) What is the principal use of the drug warfarin?
   a) As an anti-coagulant
   b) As a tranquilliser
   c) As an antacid

10) What does a sphygmomanometer measure?
   a) Brain activity
   b) Hearing
   c) Blood pressure

EXPERT

Answers: 1c, 2b, 3b, 4c, 5b, 6a, 7a, 8a, 9a, 10c

PHYSICS

EXPERT

1) Which scientist was the first to postulate that everything was built of atoms?
   a) Leucippus of Miletus
   b) Democritus of Abdera
   c) Isaac Newton

2) What was the first man-made object to break the sound barrier?
   a) An aeroplane
   b) A bullet
   c) A whip

3) What kind of energy is contained in a moving mass?
   a) Potential energy
   b) Kinetic energy
   c) Internal energy

4) What is the name of the negative particle circling the nucleus of an atom?
   a) Neutron
   b) Proton
   c) Electron

5) What is the name of the force that binds atomic nuclei together?
   a) Gravitation
   b) Weak nuclear force
   c) Strong nuclear force

6) Which of the following do not travel through a vacuum?
   a) Radio waves
   b) Magnetic waves
   c) Sound waves

7) What colour light has the highest frequency?
   a) Violet
   b) Red
   c) Indigo

8) Planck's constant is represented by which lower case letter?
   a) p
   b) h
   c) t

9) What type of particle is an electron?
   a) A gluon
   b) A quark
   c) A lepton

10) Which particles come in forms known as up, down, top, bottom, charm and strange?
   a) Muons
   b) Quarks
   c) Bosons

EXPERT

Answers: 1b, 2c, 3b, 4c, 5c, 6c, 7a, 8b, 9c, 10b

PLANETS

EXPERT

1) When was the planet Pluto discovered?
   a) 1781
   b) 1846
   c) 1930

2) Which planet is 5th from the Sun?
   a) Jupiter
   b) Mars
   c) Saturn

3) Which planet orbits the sun once every 88 days?
   a) Mars
   b) Venus
   c) Mercury

4) When was the planet Pluto's single satellite discovered?
   a) 1930
   b) 1953
   c) 1978

5) On which planet is the volcano Olympus Mons?
   a) Earth
   b) Mars
   c) Venus

6) Which planet takes 165 years to orbit the sun?
   a) Uranus
   b) Neptune
   c) Pluto

7) Which planet is surrounded by clouds of sulphuric acid?
   a) Venus
   b) Uranus
   c) Neptune

8) Which planet has the two satellites named Phobos and Deimos?
   a) Neptune
   b) Saturn
   c) Mars

9) Which planet contains the 'Great Dark Spot'?
   a) Neptune
   b) Jupiter
   c) Uranus

10) Which planet orbits the sun at a speed of approximately 110,000 kph?
   a) Venus
   b) Mars
   c) Earth

EXPERT

Answers: 1c, 2a, 3c, 4c, 5b, 6b, 7a, 8c, 9a, 10c

WEATHER

EXPERT

1) **What is measured by an anemometer?**
   a) Rainfall
   b) Atmospheric pressure
   c) Wind speed

2) **Where was the 20th century's highest temperature of 136° recorded in 1922?**
   a) Pad Idan, Pakistan
   b) Death Valley, California
   c) Al Aziziyah, Libya

3) **From which language does the word 'monsoon', meaning a season of rain, originate?**
   a) Arabic
   b) Cantonese
   c) Hindi

4) **What is the name of the area of low atmospheric pressure along the equator where calm winds can suddenly become storms?**
   a) The Tropic of Cancer
   b) The Doldrums
   c) The Sargasso Sea

5) **Why was the term El Niño, which can be translated as 'the little boy', originally coined for the warm ocean current off the coast of South America?**
   a) It begins slowly and then 'grows up'
   b) Its effect is to make things flourish
   c) It appears around Christmas and is a reference to the Christ Child

6) Snowflakes form regular patterns of how many sides?
   a) Six
   b) Eight
   c) Twelve

7) Why is Luke Howard remembered by meteorologists?
   a) He was the BBC's first weather forecaster
   b) He invented the classification system for clouds
   c) He was the first Professor of Meteorology at Cambridge

8) What is the name for a line on a weather map that connects two points of equal temperature?
   a) Isotherm
   b) Isobar
   c) Isobront

9) What does the Saffir-Simpson scale measure?
   a) Rainfall
   b) Fog intensity
   c) Hurricanes

10) Strictly speaking, the word 'hurricane' should be used only to describe storms in which ocean?
   a) Atlantic
   b) Pacific
   c) Indian

EXPERT

Answers: 1c, 2c, 3a, 4b, 5c, 6a, 7b, 8a, 9c, 10a

SPORT

BOXING

1) Who did Muhammad Ali (then Cassius Clay) defeat to win his first world heavyweight title?
   a) Floyd Patterson
   b) Sonny Liston
   c) Rocky Marciano

2) Who was the only undefeated world heavyweight champion of the last hundred years, winning all 49 of the professional bouts he fought?
   a) Muhammad Ali
   b) Joe Louis
   c) Rocky Marciano

3) Which world heavyweight champion was nicknamed 'The Manassas Mauler'?
   a) Joe Louis
   b) Jack Dempsey
   c) Jack Johnson

4) Which country was Lennox Lewis representing when he won his Olympic gold medal for boxing in 1988?
   a) Canada
   b) Great Britain
   c) USA

5) At what weight did Henry Cooper fight as a professional?
   a) Heavyweight
   b) Middleweight
   c) Lightweight

NOVICE

6) What was the name given to the Muhammad Ali v. George Foreman title fight in 1974?
   a) The Fight of the Century
   b) The Rumble in the Jungle
   c) The Thriller in Manila

7) How was legendary 1940s and 1950s boxer Walter Smith Jr better known?
   a) Sugar Ray Leonard
   b) Rocky Marciano
   c) Sugar Ray Robinson

8) At how many different weight divisions did Sugar Ray Leonard win world titles?
   a) 5
   b) 4
   c) 3

9) How did Bombardier Billy Wells reach an even bigger audience after his boxing career ended?
   a) He became an actor in London pantomimes
   b) He was the BBC's first boxing commentator
   c) He banged the gong at the beginning of Rank films

10) In which Elvis Presley film does he play a boxer?
   a) *Kid Galahad*
   b) *Jailhouse Rock*
   c) *Follow That Dream*

NOVICE

Answers: 1b, 2c, 3b, 4a, 5a, 6b, 7c, 8a, 9c, 10a

CRICKET

EXPERT

1) Who has captained England in the most test matches?
   a) Peter May
   b) Mike Brearley
   c) Mike Atherton

2) Who won the 2003 Cricket World Cup?
   a) Australia
   b) England
   c) South Africa

3) Which English bowler was at the centre of the 'bodyline' controversy in the 1930s?
   a) Freddie Trueman
   b) Harold Larwood
   c) Wilfred Rhodes

4) In which English city is the Edgbaston cricket ground?
   a) Manchester
   b) Sheffield
   c) Birmingham

5) The legendary Victorian cricketer W. G. Grace captained England at cricket and what other sport?
   a) Bowls
   b) Real Tennis
   c) Billiards

6) Which West Indian player hit six sixes in an over during a county championship match in 1968?
   a) Clive Lloyd
   b) Gary Sobers
   c) Rohan Kanhai

7) Which team holds the record for the highest score – 952 for six – in a Test match?
   a) Sri Lanka
   b) Australia
   c) England

8) For which Test team does the spin bowler Muttiah Muralitharan play?
   a) India
   b) Pakistan
   c) Sri Lanka

EXPERT

9) Who was the first cricketer to play in a hundred test matches?
   a) Colin Cowdrey (England)
   b) Allan Border (Australia)
   c) Sunil Gavaskar (India)

10) Who is the only player to score a double century and a century on his Test match debut?
   a) Don Bradman (Australia)
   b) Lawrence Rowe (West Indies)
   c) Zaheer Abbas (Pakistan)

Answers: 1c, 2a, 3b, 4c, 5a, 6b, 7a, 8c, 9a, 10b

ENGLISH HORSE RACING

NOVICE

1) Which of the following races is not one of the five 'Classics' of English racing?
   a) The Oaks
   b) The Cheltenham Gold Cup
   c) The St. Leger

2) Which of the Classic flat races is the oldest?
   a) The Derby
   b) The 2,000 Guineas
   c) The St. Leger

3) In which year was the first Grand National run?
   a) 1839
   b) 1776
   c) 1901

4) What is the official name for jump racing?
   a) Steeplechasing
   b) Hurdle Races
   c) National Hunt

5) Which of these races is for fillies only?
   a) The Derby
   b) The 2,000 Guineas
   c) The Oaks

---

6) How many times did Lester Piggott win the English Derby?
   a) Seven
   b) Eight
   c) Nine

7) Which of these racecourses runs both flat and jump races?
   a) Ascot
   b) Aintree
   c) Goodwood

8) Which famous racehorse won the Cheltenham Gold Cup three years in succession in the 1960s?
   a) *Red Rum*
   b) *Desert Orchid*
   c) *Arkle*

9) Which is said to be the oldest racecourse in England, with horse racing going back to 1539?
   a) Uttoxeter
   b) Chester
   c) Chepstow

10) Which king made Newmarket a racing centre?
    a) Charles II
    b) George IV
    c) Edward VII

NOVICE

Answers: 1b, 2c, 3a, 4c, 5c, 6c, 7a, 8c, 9c, 10a

FOOTBALL 1

1) In which European city is the Bernabeu Stadium?
   a) Madrid
   b) Barcelona
   c) Paris

2) For which team did David Beckham make his Football League debut, while on loan from Manchester United?
   a) Preston North End
   b) Blackburn Rovers
   c) Bolton Wanderers

NOVICE

3) Which club was replaced in the Football League by Oxford United in 1962?
   a) Barrow
   b) Darlington
   c) Accrington Stanley

4) In 1970 which was the first African nation ever to qualify for the World Cup finals?
   a) Morocco
   b) Cameroon
   c) Tunisia

5) Which English team won the European Cup Winners' Cup in 1970?
   a) Aston Villa
   b) West Ham United
   c) Manchester City

6) Who was the last player to score an international goal at Wembley?
   a) Roberto di Matteo
   b) Dietmar Hamann
   c) Marcelo Salas

7) Who was captain of Liverpool when they won the league championship in 1972–1973?
   a) Phil Thompson
   b) Tommy Smith
   c) Emlyn Hughes

8) In which country were the 1986 World Cup Finals scheduled to be held before the authorities there confessed they could not afford to stage them?
   a) Colombia
   b) Uruguay
   c) Chile

9) Who was manager of Aston Villa when they won the European Cup in May 1982?
   a) Ron Saunders
   b) Tony Barton
   c) Ron Atkinson

10) How many times did Bobby Moore captain England?
   a) 40
   b) 60
   c) 90

NOVICE

Answers: 1a, 2a, 3c, 4a, 5c, 6b, 7b, 8a, 9b, 10c

FOOTBALL 2

1) In which year did Leeds United lose to Sunderland in the FA Cup Final?
   a) 1971
   b) 1972
   c) 1973

2) From which club did Manchester United sign Cristiano Ronaldo in 2003?
   a) Benfica
   b) Porto
   c) Sporting Lisbon

3) Who scored a hat-trick when England beat Germany 5-1 in September 2001?
   a) Emile Heskey
   b) Michael Owen
   c) David Beckham

4) What nationality is Pavel Nedved?
   a) Czech
   b) Croatian
   c) Hungarian

5) Which England international of the 1980s was nicknamed Captain Marvel?
   a) Ray Wilkins
   b) Kevin Keegan
   c) Bryan Robson

NOVICE

6) Which Italian club signed Paul Gascoigne in 1992?
   a) Lazio
   b) AC Milan
   c) Juventus

7) Which is the only non-English club to win the English FA Cup?
   a) Berwick Rangers
   b) Queen's Park
   c) Cardiff City

8) What was the first club managed by Sir Alex Ferguson?
   a) East Stirling
   b) St. Mirren
   c) Aberdeen

9) Which Football League team used to play its home matches at Boothferry Park?
   a) Torquay United
   b) Hull City
   c) Plymouth Argyle

10) Who was the top scorer in the 1996 European Championships?
   a) Hristo Stoichkov
   b) Jurgen Klinsmann
   c) Alan Shearer

NOVICE

Answers: 1c, 2c, 3b, 4a, 5c, 6a, 7c, 8a, 9b, 10c

FOOTBALL CLUB NICKNAMES

Which football clubs have the following nicknames?

NOVICE

1) **The Blades**
   a) Sheffield Wednesday
   b) Sheffield United
   c) Barnsley

2) **The Addicks**
   a) Charlton Athletic
   b) Dunfermline Athletic
   c) Oldham Athletic

3) **The Bees**
   a) Brighton and Hove Albion
   b) Birmingham City
   c) Brentford

4) **The Saddlers**
   a) Luton Town
   b) Northampton Town
   c) Walsall

5) **The Tigers**
   a) Hull City
   b) York City
   c) Bristol City

6) The Bairns
   a) East Fife
   b) Falkirk
   c) Forfar Athletic

7) The Toffees
   a) Liverpool
   b) Everton
   c) Millwall

8) The Rams
   a) Leicester City
   b) Nottingham Forest
   c) Derby County

9) The Canaries
   a) Ipswich Town
   b) Norwich City
   c) Cardiff City

10) The Bully Wee
   a) Clyde
   b) Raith Rovers
   c) Queen of the South

NOVICE

Answers: 1b, 2a, 3c, 4c, 5a, 6b, 7b, 8c, 9b, 10a

FOOTBALL HISTORY

EXPERT

1) Who was the first million-pound signing in English football?
   a) Trevor Francis
   b) Kevin Keegan
   c) Denis Law

2) Which country won the first ever World Cup in 1930?
   a) Italy
   b) Brazil
   c) Uruguay

3) How did Tommy Hutchison distinguish himself in the 1981 FA Cup Final?
   a) He was sent off
   b) He scored for both sides
   c) He scored a hat-trick

4) Which is the oldest club still playing in the Football League?
   a) Notts County
   b) Everton
   c) Blackburn Rovers

5) In which year was the FA Cup final first played at Wembley?
   a) 1899
   b) 1930
   c) 1923

6) Which European team was the first non-British side to beat England in a home international?
   a) Italy
   b) Germany
   c) Hungary

7) Which goalkeeper was the first to save a penalty in an FA Cup Final?
   a) Pat Jennings
   b) Dave Beasant
   c) David Seaman

8) Who was the first footballer to be knighted?
   a) Stanley Matthews
   b) Bobby Charlton
   c) Bobby Moore

9) Which team did Brazil beat in the 1970 World Cup Final?
   a) West Germany
   b) Argentina
   c) Italy

10) Which Scottish team twice reached the English FA Cup Final in the 1880s and were twice beaten by Blackburn Rovers?
   a) Queen's Park
   b) Dundee United
   c) Rangers

EXPERT

Answers: 1a, 2c, 3b, 4a, 5c, 6c, 7b, 8a, 9c, 10a

GOLF

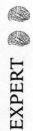

1) What is 'Tiger' Woods's real name?
   a) Eric
   b) Elric
   c) Eldrick

2) Which US Open winner was killed in a plane crash in 1999?
   a) Curtis Strange
   b) Payne Stewart
   c) Fuzzy Zoeller

3) In which country is the Dunlop Phoenix tournament held?
   a) Japan
   b) USA
   c) South Africa

4) In which year did Tony Jacklin win the British Open?
   a) 1967
   b) 1969
   c) 1971

5) Who captained the European team that won the Ryder Cup in 2002?
   a) Seve Ballesteros
   b) Sam Torrance
   c) Ian Woosnam

6) Which Scottish golf course has a hole nicknamed 'the Postage Stamp'?
   a) Muirfield
   b) Troon
   c) St. Andrews

7) Which of the following is a word used for a score of three under par on a golf hole?
   a) Eagle
   b) Albatross
   c) Condor

EXPERT

8) Which of the following golfers won the US PGA Championship five times in the 1920s?
   a) Bobby Locke
   b) Sam Snead
   c) Walter Hagen

9) Which of the following is England's oldest golf club?
   a) Royal Blackheath
   b) Royal Liverpool
   c) Royal St. Georges

10) Of which major championship was Horton Smith the first winner?
   a) British Open
   b) US Masters
   c) US PGA Championship

Answers: 1c, 2b, 3a, 4b, 5b, 6b, 7b, 8c, 9a, 10b

OLYMPICS 1

1) What was the name of the French nobleman who initiated the revival of the Olympic Games in the 1890s?
   a) De Richelieu
   b) De Lesseps
   c) De Coubertin

2) Which US swimmer won a record seven gold medals in the 1972 Munich Olympics?
   a) Mark Spitz
   b) John Naber
   c) Don Schollander

EXPERT

3) In which year did women first compete in the Olympic Games?
   a) 1900
   b) 1908
   c) 1920

4) In which event did Bob Beamon hold the olympic and world records for twenty three years?
   a) Triple jump
   b) High jump
   c) Long jump

5) Which of the following cities has hosted the Olympic Games twice?
   a) London
   b) Moscow
   c) Rome

6) Which of the following sports was introduced to the Olympics as a medal sport at the Atlanta Games in 1996?
   a) Table tennis
   b) Synchronised swimming
   c) Mountain biking

7) Which country won the soccer gold medal at the 2000 Olympics in Sydney?
   a) Cameroon
   b) Spain
   c) Japan

8) Which of the following sports was an Olympic sport from 1900 to 1920?
   a) Croquet
   b) Tug of War
   c) Lacrosse

9) Who won the 5,000m, the 10,000m and the marathon in the 1952 Olympics?
   a) Paavo Nurmi
   b) Abebe Bikila
   c) Emil Zatopek

10) Where were the Winter Olympics held in 1984?
   a) Garmisch-Partenkirchen
   b) Sarajevo
   c) St. Moritz

Answers: 1c, 2a, 3a, 4c, 5a, 6c, 7a, 8b, 9c, 10b

EXPERT

OLYMPICS 2

1) How many nations competed in the first modern Olympic Games in Athens in 1896?
   a) 14
   b) 20
   c) 31

2) At which Olympic Games did Lynn Davies win the long jump gold medal for Great Britain?
   a) Helsinki 1956
   b) Rome 1960
   c) Tokyo 1964

3) What is the Latin motto of the Olympic movement?
   a) Per Ardua ad Astra
   b) Ad Valorem
   c) Citius, Altius, Fortius

4) In which sport did the Australian Dawn Fraser win eight medals in three Olympic Games?
   a) Rowing
   b) Athletics
   c) Swimming

5) Which of the following was once a medal sport at the Olympics?
   a) Chess
   b) Billiards
   c) Golf

6) Who won both the Men's 400m and the Men's 800m at the 1976 Montreal Olympics?
   a) Steve Ovett
   b) Alberto Juantorena
   c) Butch Reynolds

7) Who won the Men's 100m at the 2000 Olympics in Sydney?
   a) Maurice Greene
   b) Ato Boldon
   c) Obadele Thompson

GENIUS

8) What was surprising about John Boland's winning of a gold medal for tennis in the 1896 Games?
   a) He only had one leg
   b) He had originally travelled to the Games only to watch not to compete
   c) He was the only competitor

9) Who was the first female gymnast to gain a perfect score of 10.00 in an Olympic competition?
   a) Olga Korbut
   b) Nadia Comaneci
   c) Ludmilla Tourischeva

10) How many Olympic gold medals has Steve Redgrave won?
   a) Three
   b) Four
   c) Five

Answers: 1a, 2c, 3c, 4c, 5c, 6b, 7a, 8b, 9b, 10c

RUGBY

1) Which All Black player scored four tries against England in the semi-final of the 1995 Rugby Union World Cup?
   a) Andrew Mehrtens
   b) Jonah Lomu
   c) Sean Fitzpatrick

2) Who won the rugby gold medal in 1924, the last time it was played at the Olympics?
   a) Australia
   b) France
   c) USA

GENIUS

3) In which year did a number of clubs in northern England break away from the Rugby Union, leading to the founding of Rugby League as a separate sport?
   a) 1895
   b) 1906
   c) 1924

4) Which national rugby union team is nicknamed the Pumas?
   a) Argentina
   b) Italy
   c) Uruguay

5) What was the name of the stadium in which the 2003 Rugby World Cup final between England and Australia was played?
   a) Melstra Stadium
   b) Velstra Stadium
   c) Telstra Stadium

6) What is the name of the Wigan Rugby League team?
   a) Wigan Wanderers
   b) Wigan Warriors
   c) Wigan Wildcats

7) Which of the following represented Wales as a sprinter in the 1970 Commonwealth Games and was also a Welsh Rugby Union international winger?
   a) J. J. Williams
   b) J. P. R. Williams
   c) Ivor Williams

8) Who was the first English player to win 50 international caps?
   a) Jonny Wilkinson
   b) Rob Andrew
   c) Rory Underwood

9) Which Irish team caused a major upset when it beat the touring New Zealand All Blacks in 1978?
   a) Ulster
   b) Leinster
   c) Munster

10) How many points was a dropped goal worth in Rugby Union until 1948?
   a) One
   b) Two
   c) Four

GENIUS

Answers: 1b, 2c, 3a, 4a, 5c, 6b, 7a, 8c, 9c, 10c

SPORT 1

1) In Rugby League, how many points is a drop goal worth?
   a) 3
   b) 2
   c) 1

2) Which British driver won the 1992 Formula One World Drivers Championship?
   a) Damon Hill
   b) Nigel Mansell
   c) Jackie Stewart

3) Which famous sports team was originally known as 'The Savoy Big Five'?
   a) The New York Yankees
   b) The Harlem Globetrotters
   c) The New York Knickerbockers

4) In which sport is Lance Armstrong a champion?
   a) Cycling
   b) Boxing
   c) Athletics

5) On a dartboard which number is directly opposite 20?
   a) 3
   b) 2
   c) 1

NOVICE

6) In which country is there a leading football club called Boca Juniors?
   a) Brazil
   b) Argentina
   c) Mexico

7) Which athletics event includes a water obstacle?
   a) 3000m steeplechase
   b) 10,000m
   c) Decathlon

8) At which sport was Jonah Barrington a world champion?
   a) Badminton
   b) Squash
   c) Table tennis

9) Of which sports commentator did Clive James once remark, 'In his quieter moments, he sounds like his trousers are on fire'?
   a) Murray Walker
   b) Jonathan Pearce
   c) David Coleman

10) In snooker how many points is the blue ball worth?
   a) Four
   b) Five
   c) Six

NOVICE

Answers: 1c, 2b, 3b, 4a, 5a, 6b, 7a, 8b, 9a, 10b

SPORT 2

1) In which sport do competitors annually compete for Doggett's Coat and Badge?
   a) Croquet
   b) Rowing
   c) Shooting

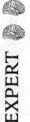

2) How many players are there in a Rugby League team?
   a) 11
   b) 13
   c) 15

EXPERT

3) Who is the only player ever to have scored a hat-trick in a Wembley FA Cup final?
   a) Stan Mortensen
   b) Geoff Hurst
   c) Jimmy Greaves

4) In which game do players compete for the Swaythling Cup?
   a) Polo
   b) Basketball
   c) Table tennis

5) During a hockey bully-off, how many times must the sticks touch?
   a) Five
   b) Two
   c) Three

6) Which score in cricket is known as a nelson?
   a) 333
   b) 222
   c) 111

7) Who has been President of the British Olympic Association since 1983?
   a) Princess Anne
   b) Prince Charles
   c) Prince Philip

EXPERT

8) Where was Britain's first motor-racing circuit, opened in 1907?
   a) Silverstone
   b) Brands Hatch
   c) Brooklands

9) Which football league team played their home matches at Burnden Park until 1997?
   a) Bolton Wanderers
   b) Blackburn Rovers
   c) Oldham Athletic

10) Which of the following South African cricketers also played for Ireland in the Benson and Hedges Cup?
   a) Shaun Pollock
   b) Jonty Rhodes
   c) Hansie Cronje

Answers: 1b, 2b, 3a, 4c, 5c, 6c, 7a, 8c, 9a, 10c

SPORT 3

1) Who did Steve Davis beat in the final when he won his first world snooker championship in 1981?
   a) Cliff Thorburn
   b) Doug Mountjoy
   c) Dennis Taylor

2) In a decathlon which is the final event?
   a) 1500m
   b) Long Jump
   c) 100m

EXPERT

3) Imran Khan played cricket for Sussex and which other county side?
   a) Yorkshire
   b) Warwickshire
   c) Worcestershire

4) Which sporting trophy was first won by Spencer Gore in 1877?
   a) British Open Golf Championship
   b) World Heavyweight Boxing Championship
   c) Wimbledon Men's Singles

5) Following Roger Bannister's breaking of the barrier, who was the second man to run a mile in less than four minutes?
   a) Derek Ibbotson
   b) John Landy
   c) Chris Chataway

6) Which legendary baseball player was nicknamed 'The Georgia Peach'?
   a) Babe Ruth
   b) Ty Cobb
   c) Joe DiMaggio

7) In which sport do toxophilists compete?
   a) Archery
   b) Clay pigeon shooting
   c) Water polo

8) Where is the Welsh Grand National run?
   a) Chester
   b) Bangor
   c) Chepstow

9) Who did Virginia Wade beat in the final to win her 1977 Wimbledon women's singles title?
   a) Billie Jean King
   b) Betty Stove
   c) Martina Navratilova

10) In which of the following sports are there British teams called Hildon Sport and Black Bears?
   a) Volleyball
   b) Netball
   c) Polo

EXPERT

Answers: 1b, 2a, 3c, 4c, 5b, 6b, 7a, 8c, 9b, 10c

SPORT 4

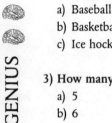

1) Why are Dundee United FC nicknamed 'the Arabs'?
   a) They used to play on a very sandy pitch
   b) They used to be owned by an Arab oil sheik
   c) Their ground is on Arabian Road

2) What sport do the New Jersey Devils and the San Jose Sharks play?
   a) Baseball
   b) Basketball
   c) Ice hockey

3) How many players are there in a volleyball team?
   a) 5
   b) 6
   c) 7

4) Which English football club was originally known as Thames Ironworks?
   a) Tottenham Hotspur
   b) Millwall
   c) West Ham United

5) Who was the first England footballer to be sent off in an international match?
   a) Alan Mullery
   b) Ray Wilkins
   c) Alan Ball

6) In which country did the sport Jai-Alai originate?
   a) Spain
   b) Japan
   c) Korea

7) Which game is thought to have been invented in 1875 by a British army officer stationed in India?
   a) Snooker
   b) Table tennis
   c) Polo

8) The footballing Neville brothers of Manchester United have a sister, Tracey, who has played for England in which sport?
   a) Basketball
   b) Hockey
   c) Netball

9) Which British prime minister played first-class cricket for Middlesex?
   a) John Major
   b) Anthony Eden
   c) Sir Alec Douglas-Home

10) In which city were the 1920 Olympic Games held?
   a) Paris
   b) Stockholm
   c) Antwerp

Answers: 1a, 2c, 3b, 4c, 5a, 6a, 7a, 8c, 9c, 10c

GENIUS

SPORT 5

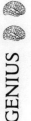

GENIUS

1) In curling what is a 'bonspiel'?
   a) A competition consisting of several matches
   b) A device used to sweep the ice
   c) A line from which shots are played

2) In which sport was Neil Adams a British champion in the 1980s?
   a) Judo
   b) Swimming
   c) Boxing

3) Which of the following West Indian cricketers has the middle name of St. Aubrun?
   a) Clive Lloyd
   b) Brian Lara
   c) Gary Sobers

4) Which is the first bridge under which the crews pass in the University Boat Race?
   a) Hammersmith Bridge
   b) Barnes Bridge
   c) Chiswick Bridge

5) In which athletic event did Abebe Bikila win two consecutive gold medals at the Rome and Tokyo Olympics?
   a) 3,000m steeplechase
   b) 10,000m
   c) Marathon

6) Which sport, other than tennis, originally had its UK headquarters at Wimbledon?
   a) Badminton
   b) Crown Bowls
   c) Croquet

7) In which sport do players make 'hazard chases'?
   a) Real Tennis
   b) Volleyball
   c) Netball

8) In which sport was Donald Butcher British champion in the 1930s?
   a) Badminton
   b) Squash
   c) Fives

9) A boat from which European country won yachting's America's Cup in 2003?
   a) Norway
   b) Switzerland
   c) France

10) By what name was the 'long jump' often known in the first half of the 20th century?
   a) Running broad jump
   b) Parallel jump
   c) Distance jump

Answers: 1a, 2a, 3c, 4a, 5c, 6c, 7a, 8b, 9b, 10a

SPORTING TROPHIES

In which sports can individuals or teams win the following trophies?

GENIUS

1) **Shell Shield**
   a) Rugby
   b) Cricket
   c) Curling

2) **Stanley Cup**
   a) Ice hockey
   b) Basketball
   c) Baseball

3) **Curtis Cup**
   a) Hockey
   b) Tennis
   c) Golf

4) **Bledisloe Cup**
   a) Hurling
   b) Australian rules football
   c) Rugby

5) **Mitropa Cup**
   a) Football
   b) Handball
   c) Lacrosse

6) Corbillon Cup
   a) Table Tennis
   b) Horse-racing
   c) Squash

7) Thomas Cup
   a) Volleyball
   b) Badminton
   c) Netball

8) Louis Vuitton Cup
   a) Ice Skating
   b) Skiing
   c) Yachting

GENIUS

9) Caulfield Cup
   a) Horse-racing
   b) Polo
   c) Hockey

10) The Lugano Cup
   a) Race walking
   b) Cycling
   c) Skiing

Answers: 1b, 2a, 3c, 4c, 5a, 6a, 7b, 8c, 9a, 10a

TENNIS

1) What was legendary champion Billie Jean King's maiden name, under which she won her first Wimbledon title, as a doubles player?
   a) Mason
   b) Connolly
   c) Moffitt

2) What nationality is Roger Federer, the Wimbledon men's singles champion of 2004?
   a) Swiss
   b) Austrian
   c) German

3) How old was Bjorn Borg when he won his first Wimbledon men's singles championship in 1985?
   a) 21
   b) 19
   c) 17

4) Which female tennis player was stabbed by an obsessive fan of her rival Steffi Graf, during a match in Hamburg in 1993?
   a) Martina Navratilova
   b) Monica Seles
   c) Martina Hingis

5) Which woman player holds the record for the most grand slam singles titles?
   a) Margaret (Smith) Court
   b) Martina Navratilova
   c) Chris Evert

6) Who was the last British male player to win a grand slam singles title?
   a) Tim Henman
   b) Roger Taylor
   c) Fred Perry

7) On what surface are the French Open championships played?
   a) Grass
   b) Clay
   c) Hard Court

8) How many times did Ivan Lendl win the men's singles championship at Wimbledon?
   a) 0
   b) 1
   c) 3

9) In which city are the US Open championships held?
   a) Los Angeles
   b) Miami
   c) New York

10) Where was John McEnroe born?
    a) Germany
    b) USA
    c) Great Britain

NOVICE

Answers: 1c, 2a, 3c, 4b, 5a, 6c, 7b, 8a, 9c, 10a